Learning from the NHS Internal Market

A review of the evidence

THE UNIVERSITY COLLEGE OF RIPON AND YORK ST. JOHN

Learning from the NHS Internal Market

A review of the evidence

Edited by Julian Le Grand, Nicholas Mays
and Jo-Ann Mulligan

Published by
King's Fund Publishing
11–13 Cavendish Square
London W1M 0AN

First published 1998

ISBN 1 85717 215 9

A CIP catalogue record for this book is available from the British Library

Distributed by Grantham Book Services Limited
Isaac Newton Way
Alma Park Industrial Estate
GRANTHAM
Lincolnshire
NG31 9SD

Tel: 01476 541 080
Fax: 01476 541 061

Designed by Two Plus Two Design Partnership
Printed and bound in Great Britain

Contents

Part IV: **Appendices**   144

Tables and Figures

Abbreviations

AE	writer opinion and anecdote
A&E	accident and emergency department
CBA	prospective controlled before and after study
CC	contemporaneous comparison/controlled study
CS	case study
CHC	Community Health Council
CHIMP	Commission for Health Improvement
CSAG	Clinical Standards Advisory Group
CWAI	Cost-Weighted Activity Index
DMU	directly managed unit
DPH	Director of Public Health
ECR	extra-contractual referral
EFH	extended fundholding (pilot)
ENT	ear, nose and throat (medical speciality)
FCE	finished consultant episode
FHSA	Family Health Services Authority
HA	Health Authority
HC	retrospective or historical control study with or without contemporaneous comparison
HCHS	Hospital and Community Health Services
FH	fundholding/fundholder
IR	indirect research
LMC	Local Medical Committee
NICE	National Institute for Clinical Excellence
OS	opinion survey
PC2000	Primary Care 2000 (total purchasing project)
PCG	Primary Care Group
PEI	purchaser efficiency index
PFI	private finance initiative
PBA	prospective before and after study without controls
RHA	Regional Health Authority
RM	routine monitoring study
SFH	standard fundholding
TPP	total purchasing pilot

Acknowledgements

This book developed from a systematic review of evidence concerning the impact of the NHS internal market undertaken at the King's Fund in 1997. The work was initiated as part of the work programme of the erstwhile King's Fund Policy Institute, then under the direction of Ken Judge who supported the project from its inception.

It was partly funded by the Department of Health; we are grateful to the Department for permission to use commissioned material, and to Alan Glanz and colleagues at the Department for helpful advice. However, the views expressed by the authors are not necessarily those of the Department.

Howard Glennerster of the London School of Economics worked with us on some parts of the project and his wisdom has contributed to the conclusions. Chris Ham, Judith Smith and Marian Barnes of the Health Services Management Centre at the University of Birmingham made useful comments on earlier drafts. George Maddox of Duke University wisely helped to put the entire venture into perspective in a number of helpful discussions. Jennifer Whale pulled the manuscript together with her usual efficiency and goodwill.

Finally, we are grateful to the many colleagues at the King's Fund who have contributed their insights to what often seemed to be interminable discussions of the material, and who have patiently tolerated its many delays.

About the Authors

Jennifer Dixon is a Fellow in Health Policy Analysis at the King's Fund, London and is currently seconded to the Department of Health. She has written widely on health policy issues in the UK. In recent years she has worked, and been published, on topics as diverse as: whether there is fair funding of GP fundholders; whether the NHS is underfunded; and health care reform in the United States. Originally qualifying in medicine, she practised in the NHS until 1989 before training in public health and health services research.

Nicholas Goodwin was a Research Officer at the King's Fund between 1995 and 1998. He is a core participant in the Total Purchasing National Evaluation Team, funded by the Department of Health, and has a particular research interest in the organisation and development of primary care. His academic background is in social sciences, having completed his PhD on *The Geography of Privatisation* in the NHS in 1994. He is now a lecturer at the Health Services Management Centre, University of Birmingham.

Richard Hamblin was a Research Officer at the King's Fund between 1995 and 1998, where he worked on London's health services and on hospital waiting lists. He is now Business Analysis Manager at East Sussex, Brighton and Hove Health Authority.

Julian Le Grand is the Richard Titmuss Professor of Social Policy at the London School of Economics and a Senior Associate of the King's Fund. Previous King's Fund publications include *Evaluating the NHS Reforms* (edited with Ray Robinson) and *Rationing in the NHS: Principles and Pragmatism* (with Bill New).

Nicholas Mays is Director of the Health Systems Programme in the Policy and Development Directorate at the King's Fund and a visiting Professor both at the London School of Hygiene and Tropical Medicine and the London School of Economics. Previous King's Fund publications include *Purchaser Plurality in UK Health Care* (with Jennifer Dixon) and *Speech and Language Therapy Services and Management in the Internal Market* (with Catherine Pope).

Jo-Ann Mulligan is a Research Officer at the King's Fund. She previously worked at the Wessex Institute of Public Health Medicine. Her current research interests include public attitudes towards the NHS, and evaluating the impact of the total purchasing scheme on emergency admissions to hospitals.

1 The context

Jennifer Dixon

The National Health Service (NHS) has been no stranger to change. Although its fundamental objectives have remained essentially the same since 1948 – universal coverage and equity of access according to need – the Service has continually developed in response to wider social, economic, political, technological and environmental pressures. Successful governments are those which are not only able to identify these wider pressures, but also respond by designing and implementing policies to shape public institutions, like the NHS, appropriately.

The 1991 reforms of the NHS introduced by the previous Conservative Government represented the largest shake-up of the Service since its formation in 1948. Like other initiatives before them, the reforms were designed to respond to pressures upon the Service, in particular the growing tension caused by rising demands and a limited supply of resources. But, unlike others, they were significant in how they were conceived, their scope and content, their speed of implementation and evolution, and their reception by the Service. For example some reforms, such as allowing the NHS to purchase care in private hospitals, stretched the very notion of what a national health service actually is. But much more significant, as far as the future of the NHS is concerned, was their impact on the Service itself.

The aim of this book is to review the evidence on the impact of the three main elements of the 1991 reforms – health authority purchasing and its variants, GP fundholding and its later developments, and NHS trusts – and consider the lessons that can be learned for the future. The review is relevant for several reasons. The published evidence is scattered across several disciplines and has not before been reviewed systematically or published together. The results of this review will be timely to consider in the light of the plans for reform of the Service put forward by the Labour Government in the White Paper *The New NHS* (Secretary of State for

Health, 1997). Lastly, there has been no real discussion of the type and volume of research into the impact of the reforms, and how it could be improved to aid policy-making in future.

Before reviewing the evidence, it is important to consider the context in which the reforms were designed and implemented, as this bears on both the impact of the reforms and the type and volume of research evidence available. Much has been written about the prevailing political and economic environment in the 1980s which led to the design of initiatives set out in the 1989 White Paper *Working for Patients* (Secretaries of State for Health, 1989), which in turn heralded the NHS reforms implemented in 1991 (Butler, 1992; Gilmour, 1993; Young, 1993; Klein, 1995a; Timmins, 1995a; Glennerster and Le Grand, 1995; West, 1997). It is not intended to repeat this history here, but rather to sketch some of the key events that are relevant to consider alongside the evidence of impact of the reforms, presented later in this book.

Throughout the 1980s a Conservative Government was in power with both a strong leader, Margaret Thatcher, and, for much of the decade, a significant majority in the House of Commons. The Thatcher Government had a strong conviction that the market was a better mechanism by which to allocate resources rather than the State, and that to create a more competitive and healthier economy, lowering public expenditure and taxes were necessary. Furthermore the prevailing view of the Government, and large sections of the media, was that public services were characterised by outdated, inefficient practices, driven by narrow professional interests and were insufficiently responsive to users. The time for change was long overdue.

The activities and costs of all parts of the public sector therefore came under intense scrutiny. The large public monopolies such as the water, gas and electricity industries, were broken up and sold off to the private sector. The NHS escaped wholesale privatisation because it consistently enjoyed public support – even Mrs Thatcher conceded that the Service 'offered high quality care ... at a reasonably modest unit cost' (Thatcher, 1990) – and there was no consensus that privatisation would solve more problems than it was likely to create.

Nevertheless, significant problems were perceived as needing attention. There was an overriding imperative to curb the growth in spending on the Service to keep public expenditure down; unacceptably large variations in performance in different areas were apparent; there was a marked lack of information and choice for consumers; the Service was insufficiently managed; and there was almost no reason for the medical profession to consider the costs of treatment even though the NHS operated within a cash-limited budget. Furthermore, perennial problems such as long waiting lists and times, ward closures, staff shortages and difficulties in admitting emergency cases remained stubbornly difficult to solve.

Some attempts were made to address these issues during the 1980s. For example, following the Griffiths Report in 1983 (Griffiths, 1983), general management was introduced throughout the Service. Managers, on performance-related pay, were made responsible for running hospitals and implementing Government policy, and were directly accountable to the centre. There was a stream of directives from the Department of Health exhorting the Service to improve efficiency in various ways; for example through cost improvement programmes and cutting management costs. In 1990 the remit of the Audit Commission was extended from local government to include the NHS, increasing the scope for conducting value-for-money studies and offering guidance to the Service on improving efficiency.

Other policies introduced later in the 1980s took on a different flavour, some of which heralded the later reforms. These included giving incentives to local services, rather than central directives, to improve efficiency, although the distinction was at times blurred. For example, the resource management initiative (Packwood et al., 1991) meant devolving budgets within hospitals to clinical directorates, which would then buy and sell services from other directorates in a form of an 'internal market'. Hospitals were required to tender for ancillary services from a range of competing providers – private or public.

Other initiatives focused on raising extra income for local services rather than efficiency *per se*. For example, the 1988 Health and Medicines Act increased the capacity of hospitals to generate income from private sources, provided that this did not disadvantage NHS patients. This resulted in NHS hospitals undertaking a variety of entrepreneurial activities: expanding the number of pay beds; charging for car parking; renting space within the hospital to shops, banks and other businesses.

But few initiatives were directed at other significant problems, such as the large variations in clinical practice or the general unresponsiveness of the NHS towards patients. A start was made in 1990 with the introduction of a national GP contract, which made explicit in broad terms what was expected from GPs for the fees paid to them. More significant action to scrutinise or modify clinical behaviour was ducked, and the dominance exerted by hospitals over patients and their GPs remained essentially unchallenged.

Despite efforts to improve efficiency and raise extra local revenue, the same basic problems remained. Rising demand, coupled with the frugal real growth in funding in the mid-1980s, helped to force a financial crisis. Demonstrations by NHS staff over shortage of funds, closed wards and cancelled operations were commonplace. The media highlighted numerous cases of patients going without care due to shortages, including the case of a child in Birmingham who had a life-saving heart operation cancelled because of a lack of intensive care nurses. The stakes were raised by the Presidents of three Royal Colleges who made a public statement urging immediate government action to save the NHS from imminent demise. The crisis reached its nadir over the winter of 1987, forcing Margaret Thatcher to announce in January 1988 that a wide-ranging review of the NHS was underway.

With hindsight it could be argued that the crisis was also forced by rising anxiety and low trust within the NHS, and possibly the media, about the future of the NHS. This anxiety came from the anti-public sector rhetoric put out by the Government at the time. The statement by Margaret Thatcher that 'the NHS is safe in our hands' came too late to reassure the public and the Service. The way that the subsequent review of the NHS was conducted simply added to that anxiety, and very effectively built resistance to any proposed change. The review was conducted in secret, and there was next to no consultation with the professions represented in the NHS or independent non-partisan outside bodies, such as the universities or voluntary sector. Indeed, the review was conducted by no more than a handful of politicians and political advisors strongly aligned to the Conservative Party. The result, it was felt by many inside and outside of the NHS, could only spell trouble.

Initially everything was up for review, including the methods of financing and organising the NHS, although alternative methods of funding to general taxation and national insurance were dismissed early on and did not appear in the subsequent White Paper (Secretaries of State for Health, 1989). Ideas put forward by one visiting US economist, Alain Enthoven, as well as two home-grown ones, Alan Maynard and Nick Bosanquet, gained significant ground (Maynard, 1986). The ideas mooted were essentially about splitting purchasing from providing in the NHS, allowing providers to compete for NHS funds and to be rewarded for quality and efficiency, and giving GPs budgets to purchase hospital care (Enthoven, 1985).

The result of the review was the White Paper *Working for Patients* (Secretaries of State for Health, 1989) in which the aims of the Government's proposals for reforming the NHS were spelt out. These were to improve value for money, to reward efficient and higher quality providers and to encourage greater responsiveness of services to patients, while maintaining the founding principle of the NHS: equity of access for equal need.

The proposed treatment was widespread reform of the organisation of the NHS. The main feature was the separation of the purchaser and provider functions: purchasers (health authorities or HAs) would buy services from providers of acute or community health services (renamed NHS trusts) through a contract on behalf of their resident populations. The HAs would receive budgets from central government determined by a weighted capitation formula.

The basic logic was that as money did not automatically flow from purchaser to provider, providers would have to compete for business. The resulting competition would encourage providers to be more efficient, more responsive and offer better quality care. Thus an internal market was to be created. The term 'internal', implying that both the buying and selling of services would occur within the NHS, was not entirely accurate because NHS purchasers were subsequently allowed to purchase care from private providers. Some commentators preferred the term 'quasi' market, drawing parallels with similar quasi-market developments elsewhere in the public sector (Le Grand and Bartlett, 1993; Glennerster and Le Grand, 1995).

The purchaser/provider split was universal and mandatory, resulting in what has been called 'dictated competition'. However, other reforms outlined in *Working for Patients* allowed some local discretion. For example, GP practices could volunteer to hold a budget to purchase a restricted range of care (mainly elective surgery and drugs) for their patients, provided that they had a registered population of 11,000 or more and that they inspired confidence that they could manage a budget. Their budgets were to be withdrawn from the host health authority purchaser in whose boundaries they were located. The budgets were to be set initially on the basis of the costs of their referrals for the relevant procedures in the year prior to joining the scheme, but were supposed to move eventually to a system of weighted capitation.

This 'GP budget-holding' (soon to be renamed 'GP fundholding') scheme was essentially an afterthought by the then Secretary of State for Health, Kenneth Clarke, (Timmins, 1995a). He thought it desirable to offer patients an alternative purchaser of hospital care to a health authority. It was assumed that GPs would have more ability to lever change than health authorities, because they had more detailed local knowledge of services and because hospitals were more likely to be responsive to GPs than anonymous health authority managers. Furthermore, fundholding practices were given a clear incentive to be more efficient: they were allowed to keep any savings from their budget to use for patient care. In contrast, health authorities were not allowed to keep any savings they made, but instead were required by the NHS Executive of the Department of Health to ensure that their providers produce 3% greater activity for the same cost each year, and to reduce management costs by proportions specified by the Government. Notably, fundholders were largely exempt from these and other central requirements to improve efficiency.

Similarly, acute hospitals and providers of community health services were encouraged, not mandated, to become NHS 'trusts'. These would be semi-independent, non-profit organisations, still nominally within the NHS but with certain freedoms of action concerning pay, skill-mix and service delivery. Unlike fundholders, however, they were not allowed to keep any budgetary surpluses. Boards of hospitals were slimmed down: out went elected representatives from local government and Community Health Councils, and in came members appointed by the Government, often from the business sector and with Conservative Party sympathies, who could be trusted to make the reforms a success.

The essential elements of these changes – a split between purchasing and providing, devolved budgets, a quasi-market based on contracts – were not unique to the NHS. Many public sector institutions, for example school education, community care and the BBC, were reformed along these lines at a similar time. The main features came to be included in what was termed 'the new public management', and stemmed back to the ideas of Osborne and Gaebler (1992) in the USA, who suggested that public organisations should 'steer' (purchase, or influence the purchasing of services) and not necessarily 'row' (provide the service). But this raised heady questions within the NHS about the meaning of public service. For example could private providers (who were heavily motivated by profit), or even public providers (motivated to compete and maximise income), deliver services to meet basic NHS objectives? To many, the answer was an automatic negative, and the reforms were thought to be incompatible with the notion of a national health service.

It was significant that entry into the GP fundholding scheme and becoming an NHS trust was discretionary and not mandatory. First, it meant that only the most willing and able would join at the outset. Volunteers were more likely to be product champions, inclined positively towards the reforms in general, more able to make the policy work and thus be a ready source of good news about the initial impact of the reforms. The volunteers represented politically acceptable pilots: pilots who were interested in succeeding rather than potentially sabotaging the reforms. Indeed, the potential for sabotage, given the firm opposition by the profession, was one of the main reasons given by the Secretary of State for Health, Kenneth Clarke, for not first piloting the reforms in several regions (Timmins, 1995a).

Second, because not all GPs became fundholders and not all hospitals became NHS trusts overnight, the details of the policy did not need to be thought out in great detail before implementation. Instead, they could be filled in over time as the need arose, using the volunteers as relatively willing and sympathetic pilots. Although many called this 'policy-making on the hoof', others argued that this approach was the most appropriate and flexible given the nature of the reforms. Whatever the view, the approach relied heavily on the ability of the NHS Executive to be able to spot problems when the need arose and to make a swift response. This was possible in the early days of the reforms because the small number of trusts and GP fundholders were likely to have a close relationship with either the regional health authority, regional trust units (set up to oversee NHS trusts) or directly with the NHS Executive. Later on, as the number of fundholders multiplied, all providers became trusts and, as the number of staff in the regional health authorities and Department of Health reduced, this capacity was necessarily diminished.

Third, the policy meant that the volunteers received considerable investment to support the new responsibilities which accompanied fundholding or trust status. This included financial investment through computer and management allowances, and investment of the time and energy of managers from the local and regional health authority and local trusts. Organisations were thus rewarded financially for volunteering; resources were diverted to those which were most willing and able to take up the new opportunities, rather than to those in areas where funds were most needed. This was less of an issue for hospitals, because most became trusts by 1994. It was more an issue for GP practices, and it may have widened the gap between the well-endowed practices who joined (such as large group practices located in the wealthier suburbs) and the less well-equipped (such as single-handed inner city practices covering deprived areas) who did not. It also underlined a tendency of the Government to 'fund the fittest' – those who were more likely to be successful – rather than those who were the neediest; ensuring equity in health services was not a prime objective at the time. All of these points are important to bear in mind when considering both the methods and results of subsequent evaluation studies.

The proposals in *Working for Patients* were launched with a fanfare in January 1989 and greeted with widespread scepticism mixed with curiosity to see how they would work. The proposals were interpreted by many to be the result of a highly ideological policy to 'marketise' the NHS, and the environment into which they were launched was highly charged with suspicion and mistrust. There was predictable opposition from powerful interest groups, notably the British Medical Association (BMA), which had not been consulted. The research community was not slow to follow with predictions of the likely, mainly negative, impact of the reforms and the unsuitability and unworkability of introducing a business ethic into public service. The chorus of complaint and opposition grew louder during, and after, a brief consultation period, when the bulk of proposed reforms were made law in the *NHS and Community Care Act 1990* and introduced into the NHS on 1 April 1991.

The highly politicised atmosphere in 1991 split professional allegiances, bewildered the public, and set both against the NHS managers responsible for making the reforms work. This politicisation stretched throughout the NHS from the civil service (Foster and Plowden, 1996) to NHS managers, to the new chairs and non-executive directors appointed on to health authority and trust boards, and extended into the medical profession. Some GPs who became fundholders in the first wave were clearly aligned to the Conservative Party and were initially ostracised by their colleagues for joining the scheme. But most of the hostility from NHS clinical staff and the public was reserved for NHS managers who were charged with implementation of the reforms. Many managers were enthusiastic and, having recently come from the private sector, embraced not only business culture and jargon but the 'one of us' ethic encouraged by the Government at the time. But partly to allay fears, not least in Whitehall, the Government encouraged a 'steady state' in the first year of the reforms. For example, health authorities were not allowed to depart far from purchasing historical patterns of care. This would allow, in the jargon of the day, a 'smooth take-off' and reduce the chances of disaster.

In this environment it is not surprising that funds were not made available by the Government to allow external independent evaluation of the effects of its own highly controversial policies: conviction won over evaluation. There was thus no independent voice, such as from the universities, which could help to defuse the highly charged atmosphere by giving a more objective appraisal of events. As a consequence, for at least two years there was an inevitable vacuum of information from research – a vacuum filled by anecdotal claim and angry counterclaim from those working within the NHS. Researchers were left to muster resources where they could, with the inevitable result that investigation was uncoordinated and mostly set up after April 1991. Thus the opportunity was missed to set up rigorous studies which allowed before-and-after comparisons to be made.

Apart from a lack of funding, the prevailing NHS environment also meant that research was more difficult than usual to conduct. Managers in some cases were less than willing to share information with researchers (particularly information on costs), for reasons of 'market confidentiality' and possibly because of presumed ideological differences with university-based researchers. The rush by hospitals to achieve trust status meant that many invested in new information systems. This delayed access to routine data by researchers and may have disrupted the flow of routine data collection. As the NHS devolved into smaller units (purchasers and providers), it became increasingly difficult to obtain information from one central source, for example the regional health authorities, especially after the latter were abolished in 1995. Finally, the rapid evolution of the reforms after 1991, the delayed impact of other policies introduced before 1991, such as the 1990 GP contract, as well as the effect of policies introduced subsequently such as the *Patient's Charter* (Department of Health, 1991a) and *Local Voices* (Department of Health, 1991b) added to the researchers' confusion. They were not just unsure of *what* to evaluate but of *how* – in such a dynamic and increasingly cluttered policy environment.

The results of evaluation by independent researchers were thus not only absent from the public domain in the early 1990s, but also were not available for the benefit of the Government or the Department of Health to help understand how the policy was progressing. Instead, both relied more upon operational information gathered through the usual links between the Department, NHS Executive and the Service (for example through analysis of routine data or routine meetings with NHS managers) or through more direct links with friendly pioneer fundholders and trusts. There was an emphasis by the Government on collecting and broadcasting good news from the product champions (such as fundholders or trust managers or political appointees to trust and health authority boards), although this was swiftly countered by opponents in the NHS and by the political parties in opposition. Similarly, the earliest available external research providing favourable news was quoted repeatedly, whereas other studies were either ignored or dismissed.

However, despite the handicaps mentioned above, a steady trickle of research findings were published and, by the mid- to late 1990s, had accumulated into a modest pile. But, by this time, the purchasing and providing landscape had changed dramatically as the 1991 reforms had evolved. All providers had become NHS trusts. On the purchaser side, some health authorities had merged with each other; and all merged with their local Family Health Service Authority (FHSA). The 'standard' fundholding (SFH) model had been adapted to allow smaller and smaller practices to take part, with the limit being steadily reduced until it included practices with list sizes as low as 5,000. Partly in consequence, standard fundholding had become increasingly popular, with over half the population covered by fundholding practices by 1997, controlling over 10% of hospital and community health service spending. In addition, a new form of 'community' fundholding was introduced in 1996, in which practices of 3,000 to 5,000 patients could volunteer to purchase all the non-hospital services contained in the SFH package, and 'extended' fundholding was brought in, expanding the range of services which could be bought by SFHs. Arrangements developed in some areas in which fundholding practices work closely together, either in consortia or multi-funds. Consortia were informal alignments of SFH practices in which the practices agreed to coordinate their purchasing intentions in specific areas; multi-funds were more formal arrangements where practices agreed to pool their SFH management allowances and administrative arrangements. By 1997 there were over 50 multi-funds covering around three million people. The fundholding scheme was again extended in 1995/96 by setting up some 80 'total purchasing pilots'(TPPs), where groups of SFHs joined together to purchase potentially all the hospital and community health services for their patients on behalf of the local health authority (Mays *et al.*, 1997).

In some areas, GPs who remained ideologically opposed to fundholding formed GP commissioning groups; in others both fundholding and non-fundholding practices were involved in locality commissioning (Colgan and Rose, 1997), with or without a notional budget allocated to their locality. Unlike the case with fundholding, this occurred without the encouragement of the Government and, more importantly, without the extra resources to support the management of these groups. The increasing plurality of arrangements for purchasing was a challenge even to describe and keep track of, let alone evaluate, or indeed to begin to regulate (Mays and Dixon, 1996).

The political landscape had also changed. As the reforms bedded down, and some benefits were apparent, it became obvious that many of the changes had been accepted by NHS professionals who originally had been implacably opposed to them. Even the BMA offered muted concessions that the reforms had brought some benefits. Also, it was realised soon after 1991 that the 'internal market' itself was not really a market, and could never be in a realistic sense of the word. Competition between providers in many areas of the country simply did not exist. The tidal wave of cut-throat competition which had threatened to crash over the NHS turned out to be little more than a gentle wave lapping at its edges. Indeed, the word competition lost currency and was replaced by 'contestability' or potential for competition. However, even when such potential existed, the extent to which purchasers (fundholding practices or health authority purchasers) were using the threat of competition to lever change was far from clear. In any case, health authorities at least had a vested interest in supporting their local providers, in a relationship based more on collaboration than threat.

There was also a growing consensus that separation of purchasing and providing gave health authority purchasers some new levers to help change local services (even if they were weak in practice). Also, giving GP practices, or groups of practices, budgets had produced innovation and some tangible benefits to patients. Indeed, many practices had shown that it was perfectly possible to be a responsible and 'ethical' purchasing unit.

By 1996 and early 1997 more Government papers appeared: *Choice and Opportunity* and *Delivering the Future* (Secretary of State for Health,

1996a, 1996b). Both focused on primary care. In contrast to *Working for Patients*, these were the product of a 'listening exercise': an effort made by the Government to take into account the views of those working in the Service on the way forward for primary care. The proposals were far-ranging; for example contracts for primary care services were envisaged between health authorities and whole practices, and/or community NHS trusts where health authorities could specify the services to be provided. The White Papers were embodied as the Primary Care Act 1997, passed in the dying days of the Major Government. The new Labour Government confirmed that funds would be available to evaluate both GP commissioning groups and the new Primary Care Act pilot schemes (NHS Executive, 1997).

By the 1997 general election, a consensus had developed between the political parties that the essential features of the reforms were worth keeping – notably the split between purchasing and providing in the NHS. Disagreements were more apparent over the details. These included whether single GP practices or groups of practices in a locality would be encouraged to hold budgets, whether contracting should take place annually or over longer periods, or the extent to which the costs of administration could be reduced. Both the consensus, and the disagreements, were less informed by such evidence of the reforms as had accumulated than by political gut-feelings.

December 1997 saw the publication of the new Labour Government's plans for the NHS in England: the White Paper *The New NHS* (Secretary of State for Health, 1997). Despite the rhetoric in the White Paper that the Tory reforms of the NHS had been abolished, the high degree of consensus between the old government and the new about the merits of keeping the essential features of the 1991 reforms was obvious. The purchaser/provider split was to remain, as were NHS trusts and, although GP fundholding was to be abolished, groups of GP practices (primary care groups) covering geographical communities of up to a population of 100,000 would be responsible for purchasing hospital, community and primary care for their populations. The main differences were of emphasis. 'Cooperation' not competition between purchasers and providers would be encouraged, and annual contracts would be abolished in favour of longer term 'Health Improvement Programmes' jointly agreed between trust, primary care group and health authority. It was claimed that, as a result of scrapping yearly contracting and GP fundholding, management and administrative costs would be reduced.

So, as we enter this new phase of reform in the NHS, it seems as though there is a fair degree of consensus between political parties, and within the Service, about the value of keeping the basic features of the 1991 reforms. But how far is this justifiable on the basis of the available evidence? In the remainder of this book, we address this question by reviewing the published evidence on the impact of the reforms.

2 Methods

Julian Le Grand and Nicholas Mays

This book reviews the research evidence concerning the NHS internal market, and attempts to use the evidence to evaluate its impact. Policy evaluation requires criteria against which a policy can be judged; the first section of this chapter examines the criteria that we used. The next section discusses the way in which the material that relates to the different elements of the internal market has been organised. Finally, the concluding section spells out the methods employed to review the material.

Evaluation criteria

Many of the evaluative research studies in this area were far from explicit about the criteria they were using, and it is not always easy to see which criteria were implicit in the works concerned. However, it seems that the impact of change can be assessed in relation to five broad headings, similar to those used in earlier exercises of this kind (Le Grand and Bartlett, 1993; Robinson and Le Grand, 1994): *efficiency, equity, quality, choice and responsiveness* and *accountability*.

Efficiency

Efficiency is often identified with crude cost-cutting and so tends to be unpopular among those who actually have to provide the relevant service. However, a more sophisticated approach would acknowledge that the way in which resources are used to achieve given ends is an important matter of social concern and that, other things being equal, the more efficiently such resources are used the better.

Two definitions of efficiency are familiar to economists: *technical* or *productive efficiency* which maximises output for a given level of inputs; and *allocative efficiency* in which the best mix of outputs across different service areas is selected. Much of the criticism of the pre-1991 NHS implied that it was failing on both counts (that is, providers were inefficiently producing the wrong output). Although technical efficiency is a provider concern, the purchasing role in combination with the internal market was explicitly intended to produce a better match between resources and needs: an allocative task. In what follows we consider both kinds of efficiency as appropriate.

One particular efficiency issue concerns *transactions costs*. These refer to the administrative costs of actually operating the internal market, such as ensuring that contracts are well specified, negotiated and monitored. The term is also used to refer to the extra management and administrative costs associated with the market's introduction. Transactions costs are probably best interpreted as a technical efficiency concern; but because of the salience of the issue in the policy debate, we discuss such evidence as exists concerning these sets of costs separately.

Equity

A concern with equity or social justice was arguably the principal motivation that led to the original foundation of the NHS; no evaluative exercise can ignore the impact of the policy concerned on equity in some form or another. However, equity is a contested term and there is no universal agreement on how it should be interpreted in different contexts (Le Grand, 1991). Most of the research that deals with equity in the health care area, however, appears to adopt one of two interpretations. The first is that of equal treatment for equal need: this means that the amount of treatment that patients receive should be determined solely by their need and not by any other factor such as income, race, class, gender, etc. The second interpretation is similar, but not identical: it concerns access to care and requires that this be equal for all, again independently of any other factor. Both of these interpretations appear in what follows.

Quality

How different models of purchasing perform in relation to the quality of care is an obvious criterion against which they should be judged. *Working for Patients* gave as one of its two key objectives 'to give patients ... better health care' (Secretaries of State for Health, 1989), and it is hard to imagine this being seriously challenged as a policy goal.

However, as with equity, the criterion is subject to many possible interpretations. Quality may be defined in terms of indicators of health outcomes: the improvements in individual health that are attributable to the relevant policy intervention. Alternatively, it could refer to patient satisfaction with treatment received. It might also refer to the outputs of the system (such as hospital discharges or deaths), to indicators of the processes that patients have to undergo (such as waiting times) or to the system 'inputs' (quality of medical staff or service facilities). Here we accept that quality is multi-dimensional and report on those dimensions that have been investigated by the work under review.

Choice and responsiveness

As noted above, *Working for Patients* gave quality of care as one of the two objectives for the reforms. The other objective concerned choice: specifically, the importance of giving patients 'greater choice of services available' (Secretaries of State for Health, 1989). Greater choice may be seen as a desirable aim in itself; alternatively, it can be viewed as an instrumental aim, a tool for achieving other ends such as efficiency and responsiveness. In particular, the aim of improving the responsiveness of the system was flagged up in the White Paper. It referred to the need for those in the NHS who successfully responded to local needs or preferences to be appropriately rewarded (Secretaries of State for Health, 1989).

Accountability

That the system should be accountable seems a reasonable requirement for any public service. Purchasing and providing agents need to account for their activities to the funders of those activities. Because, in the case of the NHS, funding comes from taxpayers via central government, accountability to the centre is clearly an important issue. However, other forms of accountability (for instance, to local communities or to practice populations) are also important and have been considered by some of the studies under review. Accountability in all its aspects is difficult to study empirically and has a strong normative component. Nevertheless, we have attempted to bring together evidence pertaining to this aspect of the structure and performance of the NHS.

Methods

Published material was sought using three methods:

- searching using electronic databases (King's Fund Library dataset, Medline, Health Planning).

- searching in libraries for material not generally included on electronic databases (offprint collections, published bibliographies, unpublished reports, 'grey literature').

- asking key experts from the academic research community and from within the NHS, including all Directors of Public Health in England, to identify relevant papers, and reports.

The definition of evidence used was broad, with all published material being reviewed. This ranged from controlled statistical studies published in peer-reviewed journals through to opinion and anecdote. More specifically, the evidence can be grouped into seven categories:

- prospective, including before-and-after studies with and without control groups and contemporaneous studies with control groups (CBA, PBA, CC).

- retrospective or historic control studies with or without contemporaneous comparison (HC).

- routine monitoring (RM).

- case studies (CS).

- indirect research: systematic hypothesis generation, theoretically informed commentary and literature reviews (IR).

- opinion surveys (OS).

- writer opinion and anecdote (AE).

The studies found are listed in the Appendices and assigned to one of these categories.

There was difficulty assessing the value of the information from each category. Do writer opinions and anecdote carry the same weight as controlled studies, for instance? If not, how much less weight? In view of the difficulty of answering this kind of question, a strict ranking of studies according to value was not possible. However, when summarising and interpreting the results of published material, we tended to place a greater value on certain types of studies over others, along the lines of the ranking in the list above. Also, because of the large volume of news, anecdote and writer opinion, material was only included if the contribution was new or one which we judged to be substantial.

Organisation of the review

Reflecting the complexity of the internal market noted in Chapter 1, we examined the research evidence under a variety of different headings. These include the five different approaches to purchasing: health authority purchasing (Chapter 3); GP fundholding (Chapter 4); locality and GP commissioning (Chapter 5); and total purchasing (Chapter 6). The evidence relating to NHS trusts and to the provider side in general is discussed in a separate chapter (Chapter 7).

The evidence is used to assess the performance of the various elements of the market against the set of criteria discussed above: efficiency; equity; quality; choice and responsiveness; and accountability. In each case, an attempt is made to assess the degree of consensus amongst writers of the various merits and faults of the scheme. This assessment tries to make clear the types of evidence that have been used to fuel these opinions, and comments on the quality and strength of the evidence. Chapter 8 concludes with an assessment of how successful the different models have been in meeting the criteria and, overall, the extent to which the internal market can be said to have succeeded or failed.

The Appendices summarise the research evidence found and categorise it. Each Appendix is a bibliographic table: one relating to HA purchasing; one to GP fundholding; one to other models of devolved purchasing; one to total purchasing; and one to trusts. Finally, the Bibliography provides a full list of references.

3 Health authority purchasing

Jo-Ann Mulligan

Our search of the literature revealed fewer formal evaluative studies of health authority (HA) purchasing than of GP fundholding. This is also reflected in the fact that the King's Fund's research initiative (Robinson and Le Grand, 1994) evaluating the early stages of the reforms did not include a study that specifically looked at the HA's purchasing role. In some respects, purchasing by HAs did not really capture the essence of what the reforms meant to most people. It seemed in part at least a 'rebadging' of the previous planning system. Anecdotal pieces around the time of implementation tended to concentrate on what was happening at the front line of hospitals and GP practices. People were more interested in how the reforms would affect patients directly rather than in changes in the activities of HAs. Purchasing or commissioning by HAs was, at least in the first year or two, a more remote concept than that of GPs 'shopping around' to cut waiting lists.

Moreover, the introduction of HA purchasing was not as 'research friendly' as the introduction of GP fundholding. Fundholding was introduced in clearly defined waves which at least allowed some comparison between different periods. HA purchasing, on the other hand, was introduced simultaneously throughout the country and comparisons were impossible. Furthermore, in the first year of the reforms HAs were told explicitly by the NHS Management Executive to aim for 'steady-state': that is, so far as possible, contracts should reproduce the existing pattern of activity and referrals. In contrast, fundholders were given more or less a free rein in their first year within the boundaries of the elective procedures that they were allowed to purchase.

Another feature of the existing research is that it appears to have been directed more towards the technical *process* of purchasing rather than towards the question of how purchasing affects the population's health or even the provision of health care compared to the previous system based on planning. This is not surprising, given that the initial concerns of most purchasers were much more to do with gaining the basic information required to establish contracts and contracting arrangements.

Consequently, most of the evidence presented here consists of indirect research, descriptive case studies and opinion pieces with few comparisons with the pre-reform situation. Although these types of evidence might at first appear unsatisfactory when compared with proper comparative studies, we should question what comparisons could or should have been made. Is it reasonable to expect flawless before/after studies, indeed *any* before/after studies when much of the data on activity, costs and quality of services pre-1991 were not recorded in any consistent way, if recorded at all? Also, the reforms themselves produced changes in the ways in which routine data were collected. Linking changes in the way services are delivered to measurable changes in outcome, although highly desirable, is almost impossible given these information inconsistencies.

Similarly, one could argue that contemporaneous comparisons with fundholders would have been confounded by the fact that the two models of HA purchasing and GP fundholding are inherently different. Fundholders purchased a relatively small proportion of the more predictable services, whereas HAs were left to face the task of purchasing everything else, including unpredictable and rising emergency admissions. Also, HAs had many roles other than purchasing, including meeting national objectives and, after they had merged with Family Health Service Authorities (FHSAs), responsibility for GP fundholders themselves. Although fundholders were allowed to make and keep a negotiated share of any savings and to use these resources as they saw fit, HAs could not keep their surpluses and were constrained by the reality that by moving much larger budgets they risked destabilising local providers. Finally, fundholders could walk away from the scheme at any time; HAs had to stay the course. In some ways, therefore, it should not be surprising if fundholders appeared more efficient, dynamic and proactive than HAs.

It is with these issues in mind that the evidence on HA purchasing should be approached. In line with the rest of the book, the evidence is evaluated according to the five criteria outlined in the introduction: *efficiency, equity, quality, choice and responsiveness* and *accountability*.

Efficiency

The question of how well HAs have brought about a better match between resources and need depends on several things, including: the level of activity purchased; their sensitivity in assessing need; the transactions costs of specifying contracts; and the quality or outcome of services purchased.

Technical efficiency

Although technical efficiency is largely concerned with the supply side, it is still worth examining to see if any increases in activity can be linked to the purchasing process. This is because the influence of HA purchasers (as the principal type of purchaser), along with competitive pressures in the internal market should, in theory, press providers to increase their output and increase efficiency.

We begin with activity. At face value, the statistics regarding NHS activity are impressive. For instance, there was a 29% increase in the number of finished consultant episodes (FCEs) per available bed from 1990/91 to 1994/95 and a corresponding decrease in length of stay from an average of 11 to 8 days (Office of Health Economics, 1995). However, statistics such as these can be criticised on several grounds. First, increases in activity purchased by HAs say little about whether an improvement in technical efficiency has occurred in the absence of accurate information on costs. Moreover, how that activity is defined can also affect the figures. Serious criticisms have been levied against FCEs as a measure of activity, the main argument being that FCEs have the potential to exaggerate NHS activity when compared with actual admissions (Radical Statistics Health Group, 1992a, 1992b, 1995; Seng et al., 1993; Appleby et al., 1993). Second, although a reduction in average length of stay may be an indicator of increased efficiency, to be really meaningful it needs to be linked with information on outcomes and readmissions. The fact that people are leaving hospital earlier does not mean that they necessarily have the same or a better outcome.

Furthermore, it is impossible to determine how much of this decrease can be attributed to the internal market and the influence of HA purchasers, and how much to other factors such as increased funding and numerous policy initiatives affecting the supply side (such as the Day Surgery Task Force initiative in the early 1990s and the Waiting List Initiatives). In essence, activity in itself says little about either the effectiveness or efficiency of the health service, although information on trends may offer some insights, as we shall see.

The Cost-Weighted Activity Index (CWAI) and the newer Purchaser Efficiency Index (PEI) are currently the only official ways in which activity purchased is linked to costs. The CWAI is obtained by aggregating the activity increases in various areas of hospital and community health services (HCHS), each weighted by the proportion of expenditure they receive (Department of Health, 1996a). The PEI is based on the CWAI and is calculated by dividing year-on-year changes in purchased health care activity by changes in districts' financial allocations.

Table 3.1 shows trends in the CWAI and an index of real resources. It is apparent that the CWAI has risen faster since the start of the reforms than have real resources (that is, there were bigger increases in activity than in expenditure). Moreover, it has risen at a faster relative rate than before the reforms. However, the index has been rising since 1982 and the large jump in 1991/92 may be more the result of better recording of activity in the first year of the reforms (from providers keen to ensure that they were reimbursed for what they carried out) than to the effect of the reforms.

Table 3.1 NHS efficiency history, 1974–96

Year	Hospital and community health services (CWAI)		Expenditure adjusted for changes in input unit costs		Change in 'efficiency'*
	Index 1974/75 = 100	Increase over previous year (%)	Index 1974/75 = 100	Increase over previous year (%)	
1974/75	100.00		100.00		
1975/76	97.14	−2.86	100.80	0.80	−3.60
1976/77	103.10	6.14	101.88	1.07	5.00
1977/78	105.66	2.48	104.81	2.87	−0.40
1978/79	106.89	1.16	107.41	2.48	−1.30
1979/80	107.07	0.18	107.43	0.01	0.20
1980/81	113.23	5.75	108.25	0.76	4.90
1981/82	115.22	1.76	110.74	2.31	−0.50
1982/83	114.63	−0.52	110.89	0.13	−0.70
1983/84	120.96	5.53	111.73	0.75	4.70
1984/85	124.57	2.98	111.79	0.05	2.90
1985/86	127.90	2.67	112.00	0.19	2.50
1986/87	129.28	1.49	112.36	0.32	1.20
1987/88	131.92	1.63	113.22	0.76	0.90
1988/89	133.05	0.86	114.03	0.72	0.10
1989/90	135.98	2.20	116.02	1.74	0.50
1990/91	137.75	1.30	117.11	0.94	0.40
1991/92	144.95	5.23	120.16	2.60	2.60
1992/93	149.45	3.10	123.89	3.10	0.00
1993/94	155.41	3.99	125.86	1.59	2.40
1994/95	161.91	4.18	127.60	1.39	2.80
1995/96**	168.19	3.88	129.85	1.76	2.10
Average annual rate of growth 1980/81 to 1991/92		2.33		0.79	1.54
Average annual rate of growth 1991/92 to 1995/96		4.08		2.09	1.95

Source: Department of Health.

* Column 2 divided by column 4 (i.e. change in cost-weighted activity in relation to change in expenditure adjusted for changes in unit costs)

** 1995/96 figures are provisional

Each year, HAs are instructed to improve performance by a specified percentage. It is thus no surprise that the PEI has also risen since the start of the reforms, with Department of Health figures suggesting that the target of 2.25% was achieved by the majority of HAs in 1994/95, although the Department, commenting on earlier figures in 1995, admitted that:

> ... *data quality problems in the first year of the new index mean that its initial estimates for 92–93 now appear to have overstated the gain in that year.*
> (Department of Health, 1996a)

Furthermore, as the index weights inpatient activity more than community and primary care services, analysts have argued that there was an incentive for purchasers to concentrate on the acute sector (Clarke *et al.*, 1993). This is supported by one survey of purchasers' contracts in 1994 in which 84% of HAs said that the PEI was a significant influence when contracting for services, with 45% saying that it encouraged them to focus on acute activity (Raftery *et al.*, 1994). Clarke and others have also argued that the index is fundamentally flawed because it assumes that more episodes of care are synonymous with better health and ignores other aspects of health care provision such as quality, effectiveness and appropriateness (Clarke *et al.*, 1993; Appleby and Little, 1993; Appleby *et al.*, 1993). Finally, the problem with any systematic attempt to measure efficiency remains the inaccuracy of the routine data. Appleby *et al.* (1993) have argued that poor accuracy of cost and activity data can lead to a margin of error greater than the percentage efficiency improvements that the index is intended to measure.

Allocative efficiency

It is difficult to link any increases in activity (real or artificial) to the behaviour of HA purchasers, given the presence of other confounding factors and pressures. Furthermore, PEIs provide little information on the composition of what is provided or whether the activity purchased is effective or appropriate. A more useful question to ask is to what extent have purchasers moved activity *between* providers or services to achieve overall value for money, assuming that quantity can be guaranteed and measured easily. In other words, how have purchasers tackled the *allocative* efficiency question?

In a perfect market, the key factor which guides purchasers to the most efficient producer is price. In an imperfect market such as the NHS, price is less likely to be the sole reason for purchasers to move contracts. Appleby's survey of purchasers' contracting intentions found that the most significant factors influencing their decision to change contracts were (in order of importance): the quality of the service; the ease of travel for residents; and the contract price compared with other providers (Appleby, 1994a). The same survey found that there had been little change in the way that HAs as a whole allocated their budgets *between* services over the period 1992/93 to 1993/94. On the other hand, there is evidence to suggest that some purchasers have taken advantage of their ability to move contracts and make savings by reorganising existing services between providers. Redmayne *et al.* (1993) showed that, in Greater London in particular, purchasers were able to release money to invest in priority areas by switching to more local or cheaper providers. Overall, however, there is an anecdotal impression that not much switching between providers has gone on. That said, there is still no properly documented national picture on what purchasers are actually purchasing, and how this may be changing.

Transactions costs

Most of the debate and evidence into the transactions costs of contract negotiations has been on the provider, and not purchaser, side (Wall, 1994; Audit Commission, 1995a). However, as Chapter 4 shows, evidence does indicate that HAs are likely to have lower transactions costs than fundholders (Glennerster *et al.*, 1994a; Glennerster *et al.*, 1994b). Griffiths' work on the costs and functions of HAs and GP purchasers (see Millar, 1997) suggests that the management costs of GP purchasers are on average 50–90% of those for HAs. However, GP purchasers undertake only half the number of functions that HAs are responsible for. The research showed that functions totalling about 40% of HA costs were totally different from those of GP fundholders and included the substantial costs that HAs incur in administering and supporting the development of GP purchasing. In terms of the NHS overall, it seems that the price of supporting two partially intersecting commissioning systems is high.

The growth in the number and complexity of purchasers' contracts could be considered a proxy indicator for a rise in transactions costs in the first few years of the reforms. Appleby (1994b) found that the number of contracts for 45 districts increased each year from 1,160 in 1991/92 to 3,309 in 1994/95. Similarly, the number of more 'sophisticated' contracts (block contracts with ceilings and floors, cost and volume and cost-per-case) also increased over the same period (Appleby, 1994a; Raftery *et al.*, 1994). Furthermore, evidence suggests that the paperwork generated by extra-contractual referrals or ECRs (those referrals that fall outside of contracts) has also imposed additional costs (Ghodse, 1995). However, it is not clear who really bears the majority of these costs and it is likely that a substantial proportion fall on providers who, in the early years of the reforms at least, were much less likely to have the administrative infrastructure to cope with the additional demands of contracting.

Separate but related costs are those associated with the management and administration of HAs. It is important to distinguish between the two at the outset because a downward trend in these costs (on which some data exist) does not necessarily mean a downward trend in overall transactions costs (on which very little direct information exists). The trend toward fewer and bigger purchasers has meant that HAs can take advantage of economies of scale in certain purchasing functions (Exworthy, 1993a). For example Dorset Health Authority saved £758,000 in management costs alone from merging East and West Dorset Health Authorities (*Health Service Journal*, 1992). Appleby (1994a) also found that spending on HA administration remained broadly constant between 1991/92 and 1994/95.

A questionnaire sent to Regional Health Authorities (RHAs) by the House of Commons' Select Committee on Health (House of Commons Health Committee, 1994a) sought to obtain their views on the impact of purchasing on a range of issues including the costs associated with the introduction of the purchaser/provider split. Predictably, most RHAs responded that it was almost impossible to achieve a direct comparison of costs devoted to administration before and after the reforms. One region did state, however, that the costs associated with the reforms had remained broadly constant over the years 1991/92 (the first year of the reforms), 1992/93 and 1993/94, although no mention was made of how the RHA defined and measured these costs. The situation with regard to establishing baselines for comparison has improved more recently with the first publication from the NHS Executive of the amount of money spent by HAs and FHSAs in running their affairs (NHS Executive, 1996). Overall, the cost of running HAs was planned to fall from £478m in 1994/95 to £477m in 1995/96 and to £450m in 1996/97. However, Butler (1996) has argued that management cost comparisons are still a long way from being an accurate guide to relative efficiency or performance. This is because each HA has its own specific roles and functions beyond the core purchasing tasks and these are not currently taken into account in the comparisons.

Finally, it is worth questioning how far traditional economic theory can provide an adequate explanation of how HAs respond to rising transactions costs in the face of bureaucratic incentives. Hughes *et al.* (1997) studied the nine HAs in Wales and argued that the development of NHS contracting policy is less about organisational adaptation than periodic strategic and administrative shifts deriving from the centre. They suggest that the finding that HAs have recently drifted towards more cooperative relationships with their providers does not just reflect a desire to reduce transactions costs and increase efficiency – it is at least in part due to coercive pressures from the NHS Executive. This rejection of an 'evolutionary' theory of quasi-markets implies that the future direction of the NHS may lie in the stark choice between a hierarchical vertically integrated NHS and a market in health care.

Outcomes and cost effectiveness

There have been numerous initiatives by the NHS Executive to improve information on outcomes that might in future be linked to costs. In many respects they can be viewed as a follow-up package to the main elements of the reforms to facilitate the development of the purchasing role. Following the publication for consultation in 1993 of an initial set of Population Health Outcomes Indicators (University of Surrey, 1993), the Department of Health has supported various projects to facilitate better assessment of health outcomes. Again, although there is so far no evidence to link any of these initiatives with improvements in purchaser efficiency, they do represent steps in the right direction.

Similarly, it is likely that the NHS reforms have injected a growing acceptance of the need to demonstrate the cost-effectiveness of what the Health Service actually does. This has been largely led from the centre by initiatives such as the Centre for Reviews and Dissemination, the Effective Care Bulletins and the UK Cochrane Centre. There have also been more local examples of purchasers working together to justify, on the basis of evidence on cost-effectiveness, why providers should discontinue existing services or introduce new ones (Stevens *et al.*, 1995). This suggests that an increasing number of purchasers have become more interested in improving the efficiency and effectiveness of what they purchase.

Financial management

One final measure of the efficiency of HAs since 1991 is the extent to which they have been able to manage their own finances by, for example, living within their budgets.

The annual publication *NHS Summarized Accounts* provides summary information on the financial performance of NHS HAs, GP fundholders, FHSAs and NHS trusts. Accounts are available for HAs to the end of the year 1995/96. However, they also include information on the financial performance of the directly managed units that remain under HA control: RHAs and special HAs for the London postgraduate teaching hospitals. Subject to these qualifications, the data are shown in Figure 3.1. They indicate that HAs underspent their revenue income by 0.9% in 1991/92, by 0.4% in 1992/93, by 0.24% in 1993/94, and overspent by 0.24% in 1994/95 and by 0.89% in 1995/96. This trend closely mirrored the trend of a slowing in the growth of revenue income in real terms over the same period. In contrast, FHSAs overspent nearly 2% of their income in 1991/92 and this reduced gradually so that by 1994/95 the total overspend was just under 1%.

Figure 3.1: Difference between NHS income and expenditure for 1991/92 to 1995/96

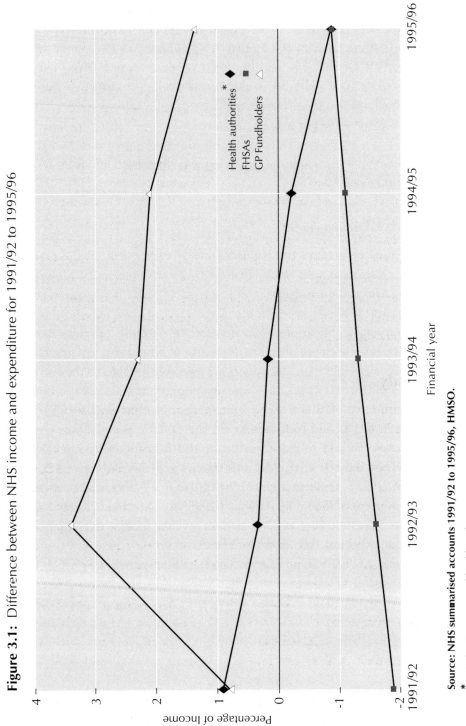

Source: NHS summarised accounts 1991/92 to 1995/96, HMSO.

It is difficult to compare the extent of budgetary control of HAs and FHSAs with GP fundholders. However, it is worth noting that over the same period from 1991 to 1996, GP fundholders overall underspent on their budgets each year. The percentage underspend reached a peak in 1992/93 at nearly 3.5% and then reduced so that by 1995/96 the overall underspend was 1.45%. As with HAs, the reduction in the underspends mirrored the overall reduction in the growth of real resources available to the NHS over the period.

There are many reasons for this difference, including the extent and type of purchasing capacity of the different purchasers and the different resources allocated per capita (see Chapter 4 on GP fundholding). Other reasons are: part of the FHSA budget was not cash-limited; HAs were mandated over the period to implement national policies for which extra funds were not available; fundholders had a more direct incentive than HAs to make savings and had a greater potential to shop around for better quality care and prices. So only some of the reasons why fundholders were more able to underspend than HAs relate to their efficiency as purchasers.

Equity

Despite equity of access to health care being a central tenet of the NHS since 1948, the new NHS inherited many inequities in the provision and use of secondary and preventive health services such as childhood immunisation (Reading *et al.*, 1993) and cervical cytology (Baker and Klein, 1991). Because HAs are charged with the task of assessing the health needs of their populations, this should encourage them to focus on equity issues by, for example, monitoring access to services for certain groups such as elderly people or ethnic minorities. The evidence which suggests that HAs are at least looking at this issue is promising. A survey of the five-year strategy documents published by HAs (Redmayne, 1995) showed that equity and accessibility were the dominant values guiding HAs in making their plans for the future. Of the 66 documents examined, 60% included equality of access or creating accessible services among their guiding principles.

Opinion surveys of health professionals on the whole, although fairly positive towards the new role of the HA as a purchaser of health care, were much more lukewarm about the effects of the internal market on the fundamental principles of the NHS such as equity (Francome, 1991; Marks, 1995). Other evidence suggests that HA purchasers appeared to be focusing more on monitoring cost and activity levels rather than examining equity considerations and that this was largely due to the financial imperatives of contracting (Majeed *et al.*, 1994). Evidence also suggests that purchasing has so far not eliminated geographical inequities in access to some specialist procedures such as coronary artery bypass grafts (Ben-Shlomo and Chaturvedi, 1995). More significantly, the Clinical Standards Advisory Group (CSAG) found that some doctors believe that the introduction of the purchaser/provider split has had an adverse effect on general equity of provision (Clinical Standards Advisory Group, 1993a; James, 1993). Unfortunately, an exact description was not given of how and why this inequity arose. Indeed, the move towards strict capitation funding of hospital and community health services (HCHS) at the HA level should have accelerated progress towards fair allocation of funds by geographical area.

Analysts have become concerned with the notion of purchasing for 'health gain' with respect to its effect on certain sections of the population. Klein and Redmayne (1992) and Whitehead (1994) both note that, although the objective of improving the population's health by maximising health gain is a desirable aim, this can have unpredictable implications for equity. Klein and Redmayne give an example of investing in health promotion policies which may have a greater impact on the well-educated middle classes than on more deprived sections of the population. There is no direct evidence to suggest this has occurred. With respect to the public health function, Whitty and Jones (1992) have argued that public health has allowed itself to be 'seduced', by the attractions of purchasing, away from the main concerns of the specialty (the social and economic determinants of health). This has led to a focus on the more immediate demands of contracting, thereby reducing the likelihood that health inequalities will be tackled.

A key question for HAs concerns the degree to which different HAs purchase different things. One good example is the provision of specialised services. In the early days of the internal market, there were fears that specialised services would become destabilised. But a recent study by the Audit Commission (1997) has shown that these fears remain largely unfounded. For example, few HAs have subjected services to tender or carried out thorough reviews that have resulted in decisions to shift contracts between providers. Yet, if the predicted problems have not taken place there have also been fewer positive gains. The Audit Commission study found that HAs had been slow to challenge providers of specialist services and influence the way that care is delivered. They argued that one of the most pressing difficulties remained the unequal patterns of access to specialist care; in many instances those living closest to specialist centres were more likely to receive treatment than those living further away. That said, the report concluded that HAs were probably better placed than smaller purchasing units to commission these low volume but high cost services.

A more visible and contentious form of priority setting is the explicit decision by an HA not to purchase a particular procedure, perhaps most memorably exemplified by the 'Child B' controversy. The extent to which this varies between HAs must have clear implications for equity. Since 1992, Klein and Redmayne have reported how HA purchasers decide on their spending priorities and what those priorities are (Klein and Redmayne, 1992; Redmayne *et al.*, 1993; Redmayne, 1995, 1996). In the most recent of these surveys they found that of 110 purchasing plans in 1996/97, 26 contained one or more contract exclusions. This compared with a figure of 11 for the 1994/95 plans. Most of the procedures listed could be classed as marginal or ineffective services (such as *in vitro* fertilisation, cosmetic surgery, removal of grommets, etc.). However, even where clear evidence on effectiveness is available, differences in access persist. A recent anecdotal example is provided by Ludlam *et al.* (1997) in a letter to the *British Medical Journal*. The authors argued that, despite the existence of evidence-based guidelines on treatment for haemophilia, widely divergent arrangements for treatment still remained. This means that the choice of treatment depended more on postcode than anything else. Clearly, it is possible to come up with many other examples and one could easily argue that such inequities have always existed in the NHS. However, HAs are probably better placed than other devolved models of purchasing to ensure that proven effective treatments become available to those who need it. If they cannot guarantee this, then the prospects for newer models to promote this kind of equity look bleak.

Quality

Perhaps the most important criterion against which the reforms might be judged is whether they have delivered a better quality of health care. But deciding by which criteria quality should be measured is problematic. This is because measures that are easy to collect (e.g. activity and mortality rates) are often meaningless without information on, for example, case severity or baseline levels from which comparisons can be made. Flynn *et al.* (1995) noted, from a study of three HAs, that these problems are multiplied when applied to areas such as community health services where there are problems in linking a specific intervention to an effect, as well as problems in defining the 'product'. They also found that processes which seemed important in the provision of services (such as inter-agency collaboration) were undermined by the mechanism of the internal market which compelled purchasers to stimulate competition between different providers.

Purchasers seemed to have faced several difficulties in maintaining and improving quality of services. First, there is the continuous pressure of an apparently inexorable increase in demand. Second, there are pressures to concentrate on issues of volume and price, especially for districts losing revenue through capitation funding (Gill, 1993). Third, a familiar theme throughout this chapter, some HAs are still finding it hard to acquire good information about the services they purchase. The finished consultant episode says very little about what actually happened to patients other than how quickly they went through the system and very broadly what procedures were carried out. It says even less about whether the care given was effective or appropriate (Clarke and McKee, 1992; Sheldon and Borowitz, 1993). With respect to commissioning specialised services, the Audit Commission (1997) found that many HAs ask only for information on processes, such as waiting times, and not for meaningful measures of patient outcome. Finally, Eve and Hodgkin (1991) have argued that using statistics from provider units ignores the fact that many clinical outcomes occur in the community, not in hospital. Also, feedback from GPs, who initiate and follow up most episodes of care, is not routinely built into the system.

Initiatives which were implemented in parallel to, or shortly after, the reforms such as the Patient's Charter and the series of Waiting List Initiatives confound traditional indicators of quality such as waiting times. It is likely that the contracting process may have encouraged some providers to meet waiting list targets, but the practice of using an indicator as a target can result in it no longer being a reliable indicator. For example, providers might aim to meet the target by other means such as lengthening the time it takes to get on to the waiting list (Appleby, 1994b). Evidence from a recent study by Hamblin *et al.* (1998) also suggests that shorter waiting lists encourage GPs to make more referrals which can then result in even longer waiting lists.

Frater and Dixon (1994) surveyed purchasers in 1993 for the UK Clearing House on Health Outcomes to determine to what extent HAs were using outcome measures in setting quality standards in contracts. They found that, although there was considerable interest in the area, there was also uncertainty amongst purchasers in finding and applying outcome measures either to determine purchasing priorities or for monitoring the quality of services used by the resident population. The initial lack of information available to guide purchasers in the development of health outcome assessment compounded the problem. Despite this, they did find evidence to suggest that HAs were using some outcome measures to aid their purchasing. Of more than 60% of HAs surveyed, health outcomes were measured in at least some of the contracts, but were formally linked to financial arrangements in less than 20%. So, few purchasers exercised leverage by imposing financial penalties (or incentives) if targets were not met.

Although quantitative evidence showing improvements in quality is scarce, numerous case studies do show how HAs have used the purchasing process to secure improvements in quality. Work by Carruthers *et al.* (1995) sought to draw together the experiences of three HAs in particular. For example, in Dorset all clinical contracts included a series of quality criteria relating to clinical effectiveness, derived from such sources as the Effective Health Care bulletins. Other service improvements included improved local cancer services and improved access to speech therapy, audiology and chiropody services. Similarly, in St Helens and Knowsley, the authors draw clear links between new structures and 'practical change' to services such as ophthalmology and neurology.

On the other hand, Moore and Dalziel (1993) showed that unpredictable results ensued when HAs used the internal market to withdraw contracts to improve the quality of services. One purchaser was unable to prevent patients continuing to use a particular service after the contract was withdrawn and the unit came under pressure, both financially and clinically. The crisis was eventually resolved, the most important factor being collaboration between purchasers and providers, not the internal market – although the latter did provide the catalyst for action. The evidence so far suggests that the internal market may have been an effective means of highlighting the 'inevitability of change' but by itself did not seem able to provide a satisfactory pattern of provision (Roberts, 1993).

Choice and responsiveness

The NHS Management Executive's publication of *Local Voices* in 1992 (NHS Management Executive, 1992) sought to emphasise the importance of giving people 'an effective voice in the shaping of health services locally'. One response to this initiative by North Derbyshire HA (Layzell, 1994) was to undertake strategy and service reviews which included the views of local people. Warning against the superficial use of questionnaires and surveys, the HA found that, by using direct contact with people who had used hospital services, they were able to address quality issues such as discharge arrangements and communication. However, the real issue is whether these findings make their way into contracts with providers and subsequently into actual practice. There is much less evidence on this.

Other direct evidence on responsiveness and choice is mixed. Freemantle *et al.* (1993), in a study of the first two years of purchasing in eight HAs, reported mixed findings in terms of the extent to which HAs had undertaken assessment of health needs. They found that HAs proceeded 'haltingly' where 'conditions are favourable' but that they abandoned it 'beyond a ritual activity' where conditions were relatively unfavourable. There is substantial anecdotal evidence suggesting there has been an increase in user forums and user representatives on both purchaser and provider advisory groups (Walsh, 1995). However, one study of health services for elderly people before and after the reforms found no increase in, for example, the choice of hospital between 1990 and 1992 (Jones *et al.*, 1994).

Fotaki (1998) interviewed GPs, consultants and patients concerning the impact of the reforms on choices offered to patients for cataract surgery in outer London and Stockholm (where market-oriented reforms similar to the British ones have been introduced). She found no increase in perceived patient or purchaser choice of either procedure or provider. Indeed, if anything, choice for both purchasers and patients seemed to have been reduced, with this effect being particularly marked in the UK. However, there was a limited increase in the amount of information given to patients. Interestingly, there were not enormous differences in any of these respects between fundholders and non-fundholders in the UK.

Redmayne (1996), in her analysis of 1995/96 and 1996/97 purchasing plans, found that HAs appeared to be placing more emphasis than before on publicising their plans to local populations. They used a variety of methods including roadshows, local press and radio and the distribution of summaries of documents to all households. Furthermore, HAs had developed mechanisms to encourage the public to register their views through representative panels and postal reply coupons. However, HAs reported less success in persuading the public to prioritise services and Redmayne concluded that:

> ... the public may not want to have to make choices between services, preferring their input to concentrate on what are important health issues for them.
> (Redmayne, 1996)

Yet, even if considerable effort is invested in trying to elicit the views of the public, to what extent are HAs influenced by the issues which emerge during consultation? Evidence on this is not easy to find. Redmayne (1996) reported that more HAs than before actually presented the results of consultation exercises in their documents and many stated that the process did have an impact. Unfortunately, little confirming evidence is provided on the precise nature of this impact.

Flynn et al. (1995) and Pickard et al. (1995) looked at the extent to which three HAs commissioning community health services viewed the role of local people with respect to health needs assessment and other aspects of the commissioning cycle. They found that, despite a willingness to involve local people, there were major uncertainties as to how this should be achieved in practical terms. Several possible limitations with regard to involving local users were identified; this included uncertainty about how to build 'local voices' information into purchasing plans and the continuation of block contracts that lacked flexibility and sensitivity to the needs and preferences of individual users. The degree of involvement and consultation is also clearly important. As one unimpressed member of a user group commented:

> Being sent a summary of the 1994/95 purchasing plan and allowed two to three weeks to respond to it was neither adequate nor feasible. (Pickard et al., 1995)

Other developments in locality-based commissioning designed to increase the sensitivity to need are summarised in Chapter 5.

Indirect research on market conditions conducive for purchasers to respond to patient wants (assuming purchasers know what these wants are!) is not particularly positive. Appleby et al. (1994) noted several reasons why we would not expect large shifts in purchasers' behaviour in response to patient wants. First, there is a straightforward lack of choice where purchasers are faced with few providers within easily accessible distance for their local population. Only 8% of acute service providers have a monopoly of the main surgical specialties inside a 30-mile radius. Second, there is a lack of detailed and accurate data to support significant changes in providers' activity. Third, the fact that any information is usually only given by the providers themselves might also make it less likely that the purchaser will act on it. Finally, patients usually express wants via their GPs, rather than directly to their HA.

Propper (1995a) also examined the incentive structures facing purchasers to determine the extent to which they seemed likely to act to increase consumer responsiveness. The key point she stressed related to the regulatory environment of HA purchasing. Where the Government monitors an aspect of an HA's performance this will increase output on the dimension being monitored and reduce output in other areas. Further, compared to the Government, individual patients and patient representatives (such as Community Health Councils or HA non-executive directors) have far less influence over the HA (Propper, 1995a; Whynes, 1993). The Government's preoccupation will be with increases in activity or volume at constant or reduced costs, whereas it is highly likely that the wants of local people will be different. Therefore, to the extent that the goals of the Government diverge from those of the local population, the local population will lose out.

Finally, there is a potential conflict between satisfying the needs and wants of the individual – the GP's primary concern – and satisfying the needs and wants of the population – the HA's main concern. The extent to which this divergence exists can be gauged by the growth of extra-contractual referrals (ECRs). ECRs can be thought of as providing a safety mechanism within the internal market to ensure that the needs and wishes of individual patients and GPs are respected. Ghodse (1995), in a study of ECRs in one HA over a six-month period, found that over £2.5 million was paid for 2,400 ECRs representing just under 1% of the total budget allocation. A disproportionate amount of this expenditure (20%) was accounted for by just 16 ECRs. These referrals suggest that GPs, on behalf of their patients, are exercising their freedom of choice but they also involve a considerable additional administrative cost. Ghodse estimated that almost £0.3 million may have been diverted from patient care to administrative processes to support the £2.5 million of ECR expenditure. Thus, if responsiveness and choice are obtained through this mechanism, it is done so at a price.

Accountability

Accountability in the public sector has always been a complex process requiring definitions of those to whom the account will be given, clear objectives for the service and a well accepted currency for assessing the service's performance (Watson, 1994). There are two lines of accountability: upwards to the Secretary of State; and a more general, but fairly diffuse, accountability to the local community and patients. The abolition of Regional Health Authorities in 1996 has meant that HAs are now more accountable to the centre in the form of the NHS Executive than before. Furthermore, although there is often a stated commitment to public accountability, Watson (1994) found in a study of HA members that this was difficult to carry out in practice. More often than not, accountability was measured by self-imposed standards rather than by genuine dialogue with the public. Overall, the upward form of accountability to the centre appears to have taken precedence over local accountability in the form of an ever-increasing stream of Executive Letters, National Guidance and directives to HAs. However, in a study of accountability in the NHS, Wall (1996) noted two issues that were relevant. First, communities and patients are only likely to hold their purchaser (GP or HA) to account in so far as the purchaser chooses to impart information and then only in so far as the patient is able to make decisions based on that knowledge. Second, politicians and governments in general often find it difficult to relinquish responsibility – at an operational as well as policy level – for public services that were once under their control. The political costs could be high if, for example, hospitals are forced to close and patients go untreated through the introduction of a market. In this context, it is perhaps understandable that the Government has often chosen to intervene in such cases.

In terms of other criteria, it could be argued that separating the purchasing from the provision of services should have improved accountability in that the purchaser sets out a clear specification by which the provider can be judged. Contracts have replaced the old hierarchical structures but little evidence exists as to how such specifications incorporate citizens' as well as patients' rights. However, recent initiatives such as 'Citizens' Juries' indicate that HAs are beginning to develop ways of involving the public directly in setting priorities (Lenaghan et al., 1996).

Although a common currency has been developed to assess an HA's performance – the Purchaser Efficiency Index – it is not universally accepted as a useful measure, even though many HAs still use it to influence activity (Raftery et al., 1994). However, some progress was made in defining objectives that at least could be more easily interpreted by the public (e.g. the Patient's Charter and the Health of the Nation targets).

In terms of the future, Ham and Woolley (1996) have proposed one way in which the public could make a judgement about the performance of HAs. They argued that public accountability would be enhanced if HAs were to produce annual reports centred on the criteria of equity, efficiency and responsiveness. These reports would summarise the performance of the 'local NHS' in each of these areas and would enable meaningful comparisons to be made between HAs.

Summary and conclusions

Although the evidence on HA purchasing is at best sketchy, most analysts would agree on the following.

- HAs as a whole are better placed than GP fundholders to plan and assess the needs of large populations.

- Although activity rose for the NHS as a whole by more than real resources since the reforms and at a faster rate than before the reforms, it is unclear how much of this was due to the activities of HA purchasers.

- There is no firm evidence on the extent to which HA purchasers have succeeded in switching expenditure between services or between providers. In many cases, fears of destabilising local providers proved to be a more pressing concern.

- Transactions costs are likely to be lower for HAs than other forms of purchasing, chiefly because they can exploit economies of scale in negotiating contracts or service agreements. But recent increases in the use of more sophisticated contracts and a rise in ECRs may operate against this.

- HAs have in general moved into deficit, unlike GP fundholders. But it is not clear whether this is due to poor financial management or to the extra pressures to which they are subject.

- There is evidence of variation between HAs in what they purchase.

- Of HAs, 60% used some measure of outcome in their contracts but only 20% linked them to financial performance.

- The opportunities for promoting choice and responsiveness appear more limited for HAs than fundholders.

- Although the evidence is limited, 'upward' accountability to the centre appears higher than that to service users or the public.

While hard evidence concerning HA purchasing is limited, some conclusions can still be drawn. First, a clear strength of HA purchasing must be their ability to plan for the whole community and to assess the needs of these communities. Moreover, the evidence suggests that the principles of equity and accessibility of health services have at least remained dominant values guiding HAs in making their plans for the future. It is this strategic overview that the Labour Government's latest White Paper, *The New NHS*, hopes to maintain through the development of local Health Improvement Programmes (Secretary of State for Health, 1997). The evidence presented here shows that HAs certainly have the potential to fulfil this task. But, the inevitable conclusion must be that HAs who work alone cannot hope to be as responsive to their populations as those which have found limited ways of devolving responsibility for assessing and commissioning health services.

The Government's decision in late 1994 to develop a primary-care-led NHS (NHS Executive, 1994a) meant that the debate had already moved on from a straight contest between HA purchasing and GP fundholding. Instead, HAs, building upon recent developments in GP fundholding and devolved purchasing, now need to consider how best to develop the so-called 'third way' outlined in *The New NHS*. Although this is probably easier said than done, it is encouraging that most HAs have already started along this path.

4 GP fundholding

Nicholas Goodwin

There is no doubt that, of all the NHS reforms, fundholding has received the most attention – both in popular debate and academic research. Much of the literature comes in the form of writer opinion, anecdote and individual case studies. Although the quantity of information from which to make a judgement on fundholding is better than that available for, say, trusts and HA purchasing, the ability to reach a conclusion on fundholding is still impeded by the lack of rigorous evaluation of the scheme as a whole. Furthermore, most research studies have focused either on the fundholders' own experiences and assessments of their achievements or on their ability to be more effective purchasers in terms of process. The information on fundholding's impact on the quality of patient care is very limited and very few studies have compared the performance of fundholders with that of non-fundholders, HAs or other forms of purchaser. There have been a number of review articles that examined the evidence on fundholding (Dixon and Glennerster, 1995; Coulter, 1995a; Hoey, 1995; Petchey, 1995). None of these, however, was a systematic review of the evidence and each covered a different subset of the available literature. So this chapter is based on a search significantly extended beyond these reviews.

Reviewing the literature on the impact of standard fundholding highlights a number of other problem areas. First, despite the high-profile nature of the fundholding initiative, there has been no centrally driven systematic effort to evaluate it. Second, the research tends to be 'localised' to specific geographical areas, making generalisation difficult as fundholding may be a better solution in some localities than others. For example, a fundholder with a choice of providers is more likely to gain service improvements than a fundholder with a monopoly provider: the former can use the threat of contract-shifting as a lever for service improvements (although, paradoxically, fundholding was slowest to take off in urban areas where choice was greatest). Third, much of the evidence on the impact of fundholding is equivocal and thus consensus exists in only a few areas.

A fundamental point to consider when attempting to evaluate the achievements of fundholding is the self-selected status of the fundholding practices. As Petchey (1995) points out, innovating practices (implying first-wave fundholding practices) were better resourced and fundholders were also more likely to be located in affluent areas than in inner cities (Audit Commission, 1995b). Fundholding practices, therefore, are not a random sample and cannot be compared directly with non-fundholders due to their relatively privileged location and background – although they do give a 'best case' indication of the potential for the model.

By giving GP practices the option of holding budgets to cover the cost of purchasing a range of mainly elective services, the Conservative Government extended the principle of separating the purchase and provision of services. In terms of expected tangible benefits, the introduction of fundholding had a number of specific objectives: reducing inefficiencies in provider organisations; creating better quality in secondary care; placing downward pressure on drug costs and unnecessary referrals; enhancing practice facilities for patient care; and promoting greater choice and responsiveness to local health needs.

Efficiency

GP fundholding was intended to encourage greater technical efficiency, yet this measure of 'value for money' has not been examined directly. In theory, GP fundholding was also intended to enhance allocative efficiency because fundholders, being more aware of the needs of individual patients, would be able to make more appropriate decisions when allocating treatments. As purchasers, therefore, fundholders would have to assess the health requirements of their local population in order to contract for the appropriate care and become allocatively efficient. However, there has been no published work examining how fundholders have used evidence on the effectiveness of care to decide the type of care they should purchase. Similarly, there has been no work that has examined how fundholders set their priorities and deploy their resources between types of care and between patients compared with how other purchasers do this.

However, there has been work on some specific areas that have relevance to questions of technical and allocative efficiency: prescribing costs;

referral rates; shifts in the location of health care provision; financial management; and transactions costs. Of these, prescribing costs, referral rates, savings and transactions costs all relate to technical efficiency; they are all concerned with affecting the costs of achieving a given level of care. Shifts in the location of care concern the preferences of patients and is therefore also an allocative efficiency issue.

Prescribing costs

The rising cost of prescribed drugs was a major concern of the Government before the reforms. In 1988, GPs spent nearly £2 billion on pharmaceuticals, an absolute rise of £696 million over 10 years (Green *et al.*, 1990). Furthermore, *Working for Patients* noted a wide differential in drug costs between regions (from £26 to £48 per head) and attributed this variation to doctors who had little interest in the cost of the drugs which they prescribed. Thus *Working for Patients* argued 'it is generally recognised that some prescribing is wasteful or unnecessarily expensive' and that a cash-limited drug budget would 'place downward pressure on expenditure on drugs in order to eliminate the waste' (Secretaries of State for Health, 1989). The Government anticipated that fundholding would have a downward influence on the rise in drug costs.

Commenting on this before the introduction of the reforms, some analysts feared that if drug costs did fall, this would not necessarily benefit the patient. Patients might not be prescribed the drugs they required, leading to a fall in the quality of care. Moreover, as Green *et al.*(1990) suggested, the economic arguments in favour of the cash-limited budget could also be flawed. They suggested that the fast growth in the expenditure on drugs by GPs nationally arose because more people needed treatment and better drugs were available to treat them with. It was argued that the best drug treatment might reduce the number of admissions to hospital, thereby significantly reducing the cost (Drummond *et al.*, 1988). Thus downward pressure on the drugs budget might be a false economy.

Many studies have examined the question of whether fundholding has had an impact on prescribing (Audit Commission, 1995b; Bradlow and Coulter, 1993; Burr *et al.*, 1992; Dowell *et al.*, 1995; Healey and Reid, 1994; Howie *et al.*, 1993, 1994, 1995a; Maxwell *et al.*, 1993; Penhale *et* al., 1993; Whynes et al., 1995; Wilson et al., 1995; Stewart-Brown et al., 1995; Wilson and Walley, 1995; Robinson, 1996; Harris and Scrivener, 1996; Rafferty et al., 1997). This research into the prescribing element of fundholding has led to two reviews of the evidence (Gosden and Torgerson, 1997; Purchasing in Practice, 1995).

There is a general consensus that, in the early years of fundholding, the rate of growth in prescribing costs was lower in fundholding than in non-fundholding practices. The Audit Commission (1995b), for example, found that from a sample of fundholders the cost of prescribing rose by 10%, 8% and 8% in 1991, 1992 and 1993. For non-fundholders the increases were 15%, 13% and 11%, respectively. It has been argued that this difference was the result of the greater use of generic drugs and reduced repeat prescribing in response to budgetary pressures among fundholders (Dowell et al., 1995). Indeed, the authors of two of the review articles accept that fundholders have been more cost-effective prescribers because of this (Dixon and Glennerster, 1995; Coulter, 1995a).

However, it has also been argued that these trends for early fundholders were not due to more cost-effective prescribing. Cost-containment measures, for example, were often delayed by the practice until after fundholding status was achieved, thereby boosting fundholding prescribing budgets because these tended to be based (at least initially) on historical spending (Dowell et al., 1995; Healey and Reid, 1994). This implies that subsequent prescribing savings accruing to such fundholding practices are likely to be inflated. Petchey (1995) and Hoey (1995) are also sceptical of the efficiency of fundholders as prescribers. Petchey, for example, points to methodological problems in the research; observations in small samples of first-wave fundholders may not be generalisable and, in some studies, non-fundholding controls subsequently became fundholders. This casts doubt on the legitimacy of the comparison practices used (Petchey, 1995). Furthermore, some non-fundholders have shown the ability to restrain the rise in prescribing costs as effectively as fundholders (Whynes et al., 1995), and Bain (1993) suggests that if fundholding was extended to low-prescribing practices then the budgetary incentive to reduce the drug budget would not be so effective and the level of cost reduction would be lower.

This argument is enhanced by more recent research on fundholding prescribing in which a common observation is that fundholders have lost the ability to reduce the rise in costs of prescribing relative to non-fundholders. The study by Stewart-Brown et al. (1995) of prescribing in the Oxford region reveals that the ability of fundholding practices to lower the growth of prescribing costs relative to non-fundholding practices reached a plateau; no significant difference now exists between fundholding and non-fundholding practices. However, these studies are not representative of the country as a whole because, in other areas, fundholders increased prescribing in an attempt to reduce referral rates. The Audit Commission (1996), in a more general analysis, concluded that the difference in drug expenditure between fundholding and non-fundholding practices was statistically significant only for first-wave practices. Indeed, it appeared that, in some locations, fundholders were becoming less effective in curbing costs than non-fundholders (Stewart-Brown et al. 1995; Robinson, 1996; Trimble and Black, 1996). Kind et al. (1993a) found that practice type did not help to explain variations in prescribing between practices; of greater significance was the location of the practice in terms of its associated FHSA.

However, the most recent and comprehensive research shifts the balance again in favour of fundholding. Harris and Scrivener (1996) analysed data concerning prescribing for all general practices in England. They found that prescribing costs were reduced for fundholders compared with non-fundholders by about 6% over the period. Successive waves of fundholders showed a similar pattern of changes: a small relative reduction in the pre-fundholding year; a maximum relative reduction in the first year; and declining relative reductions in the second and third years. After this, increases in costs were largely similar to non-fundholders but the absolute difference in levels remained. Rafferty et al. (1997) found the same pattern in a similar analysis for all Northern Irish practices. In both cases the drop was brought about by lowering the average cost per item rather than by prescribing fewer items.

The reason for the pattern of change, with a slowing of the relative reduction, may be deduced from some unpublished material produced by Glennerster in the course of the work that culminated in Glennerster et al. (1994a). Interviews with fundholders in 1993/94 revealed that most of the GPs with two years of savings had had their drug budgets reduced by the FHSA. Hence they felt that there was little point in continuing to try to make reductions. If this is a general pattern, it is hardly surprising that the rate of reduction in costs fell. In Northern Ireland, fundholders' prescribing budgets are set explicitly on the previous year's actual expenditure (Marum, 1997); so incentives to continue cost-reduction are heavily diluted, if not eliminated.

Referral rates

As well as differences in prescribing practices, the wide disparity in the rate of referrals to hospital was also of concern to the Government before the reforms. It was argued that GPs considered hospitals to be a free resource and that they did not have any incentive to be more judicious in their referral behaviour. By getting GPs to consider the costs of referral, it was hoped that inappropriate referrals would be reduced thereby reducing the cost to the NHS.

As with prescribing, there was another side to this coin. This was the fear expressed at the outset of the reforms that a constrained budget would inhibit GPs from appropriate referrals – that is, from referring patients who really did require treatment – and that this under-referral would be difficult to detect (May, 1989). Thus, although the White Paper's economic logic was to create a downward pressure on waste, the concern was that doctors would reduce referrals for budgetary savings, leaving patients without the clinical care they required. Practices could also abuse the system by referring patients to their own private clinics through the limited company scheme (later revoked), enabling fundholders to buy and sell services from themselves. Critics, therefore, pointed to the substantial conflict of interest with fundholders being both purchaser and provider (*Fundholding*, 1991; Mays and Dixon, 1996).

In addition to under-referring, many analysts felt that a cash-limited budget would lead to cost-shifting. Paton (1992), for example, suggested that practices had the incentive not to treat patients immediately but to wait until they became an emergency case, when the HA would bear the cost and not the GP practice. It was also feared that, as fundholding practices sought the best deals from providers, another cost-shift might occur at the expense of the patient: the extra travel costs to a hospital outside the boundaries of the district which provided a cheaper service (*Fundholding*, 1991).

The impact of fundholding on referral rates for outpatient care has been investigated by a number of studies (Howie *et al.* 1994, 1995a; Heaney *et al.* 1994; Coulter and Bradlow, 1993; Fear and Cattell, 1994; Surender *et al.* 1995). These studies suggested that fundholding would create the incentive to reduce referral rates compared to non-fundholding practices. However, the evidence is mixed. One study showed an actual reduction in the rate of referrals (Fear and Cattell, 1994), while the work of Howie *et al.* (1994, 1995a) showed that the drop in referral rates in fundholding practices in Scotland was matched by an increase in the use of direct access services. By contrast, work undertaken in the Oxford region found little difference in the rate of growth in referrals between fundholders and non-fundholders and found no evidence to show that budgetary pressures had caused first-wave fundholders to reduce referral rates (Coulter and Bradlow, 1993; Surender *et al.*, 1995). It is argued that the method of budget allocation may have encouraged GPs to inflate their referral rates in the preparatory year.

More recently, Ellwood (1997) looked at the influence of published prices on the pattern of referral rates in the West Midlands. She found that, despite the potential for large budget savings, fundholders seldom referred to alternative providers because of lower prices. Price was ranked least important by 20 of the 32 fundholding practices in her study. When interviewed, GPs highlighted a number of factors impeding changing their providers, not least the destabilising effect on the local providers themselves.

The evidence on referrals for emergency care is small and partly contradictory. One study indicated that fundholding had not changed the growth in emergency admissions pre-dating the reforms (Harrison *et al.*, 1995). On the other hand, another study suggested that, while non-fundholders have continued to experience a rise in emergency admissions, the rate for fundholders has not changed by as much, although the latter group did have higher absolute rates to begin with. The difference was large: a 47% increase for non-fundholders compared with just 8% for fundholders (Boersma, 1996). The incentive structure was thought to be responsible for the differences because non-fundholders, struggling to access elective services when the HA was according them at a low priority, may have been diverting cases from elective to emergency.

However, a before-and-after study in the South Western Regional Health Authority (Toth *et al.*, 1997) provided no evidence that fundholders had responded to fundholding rules by seeking to delay elective admissions, or have their patients admitted by emergency rather than elective routes. The quantitative evidence does not lead to a definitive conclusion on the overall impact of fundholding or referrals for emergency care.

The more qualitative evidence on referrals is similarly inconclusive. For example, Corney (1994) suggests that fundholders are more critical of their referral decisions and that referral rates have slowed in response to the need for 'savings'. However, Glennerster *et al.* (1992) found that the referral rates for some first-wave fundholders rose more quickly than for non-fundholding practices. A fundholding consortium, for example, was able to bargain for shorter waiting times for its patients at the local hospital but found that the growth in activity increased patient throughput and rate of referral.

Shifts in the location of health care

Many surveys have reported that fundholders offer more services than they did before the scheme was introduced, thus providing better access to care for their patients (Howie *et al.*, 1995a; Coulter, 1995a; National Audit Office, 1994; Bailey *et al.*, 1993; Macrae Todd, 1993). This growth in practice-based services has generally taken the form of greater numbers of outreach clinics taken by hospital clinicians (thus leading to a switch in the location of secondary care). However, one study has attempted to compare the growth in services provided by fundholding practices with that documented in non-fundholding practices (Kind *et al.*, 1992). This unpublished survey of GPs revealed that there was a rise in the number of clinics delivered in fundholding practices although this growth was regarded by the GPs as a response to the 1990 GP contract rather than as a specific outcome of fundholding. From other research, it is clear that non-fundholding practices have also seen a growth in on-site services, albeit smaller than for fundholding practices, and this has occurred despite the lack of access to savings enjoyed by fundholders (Bailey *et al.*, 1993; Macrae Todd, 1993).

In addition to purchasing from NHS providers, fundholders are able to use their budgets to purchase care provided outside the NHS and provide services in-house. Kerrison and Corney (1998) sought to establish the contribution of the private sector in providing outpatient outreach clinics. In a small sample of 14 fundholding practices, they found that, since becoming fundholders, ten had set up at least one medical specialist outreach clinic and 12 at least one paramedical clinic. Eight practices also reported their provider arrangements for consultant outreach clinics and paramedical clinics: 49% of the medical specialist hours and 46% of total paramedical hours were provided by private practitioners. In her study of fundholding in the West Midlands, Ellwood (1997) found wide variations between fundholding practices in the use of the private sector. She concluded that private health care had been used increasingly over the fundholding years but its use was patchy and largely restricted to a small number of fundholders. It is difficult to know the effect of these findings on patient care as there is no system in the NHS to monitor the types of activities undertaken or the relative quality of the services provided either by public or private sectors.

Some studies have suggested that greater numbers of on-site services do not necessarily mean a more cost-effective service. For example, Gillam *et al.* (1995) show that, although ophthalmic outreach care was popular with both patients and GPs and effective in filtering demand for care in the hospital, the unit cost (per patient) of the outreach clinic (£48.09) was much higher than for the conventional outpatient treatment (£15.71). Studies of integrated care projects for patients with diabetes and asthma services have similarly revealed that there was no advantage over traditional hospital care, with a higher cost of operation in GP practices (Greenhalgh, 1994; Grampian Asthma Study of Integrated Care, 1994). Moreover, a wider range of services provided in a primary care setting does not necessarily reduce prescribing or referral costs. For example, although Hackett *et al.* (1993) found that on-site physiotherapy reduced prescribing costs, Coulter (1995a) found that the use of physiotherapy services did not reduce the rate of referral to hospital consultants in orthopaedics or rheumatology. Coulter (1996) has also questioned the claim that primary care can always act as a more cost-effective substitute for secondary care. Given the current lack of evidence, shared care between primary and secondary care practitioners may be a more desirable goal than transferring care wholesale to primary care settings. However, in none of these cases was the differences in cost to *patients* (in terms of differences in travel and waiting times) measured.

If they had been, it is likely that differences in overall costs would have been lower, if not eliminated.

There is no doubt that there has been a shift in the provision of care from the secondary to the primary level. Given that this growth has occurred in both fundholding and non-fundholding practices, it is unclear to what extent this has occurred because of fundholding *per se*. However, it does appear that fundholding practices have engineered more changes in this respect than non-fundholders and it is possible that, overall, the fundholding scheme has been the catalyst for this shift. Whether the change has increased overall efficiency remains a moot point. Questions also remain on the cost-effectiveness of specific on-site services compared with that of more traditional alternatives.

Transactions costs

On its inception, some analysts predicted that fundholding would create significant financial costs to both fundholders and providers through the greater work required in negotiating and monitoring contracts, formulating purchasing strategies and undertaking general administration and accountancy work for a large number of small purchasers (Brazier *et al.*, 1990; Butler, 1992). Moreover, experience from the USA revealed that high costs were not just associated with set-up arrangements but continued into the longer term (Barr *et al.*, 1989). There was thus concern that any savings or efficiencies made by the fundholding initiative would be swallowed by higher transactions costs.

This prediction was largely fulfilled. There is a consensus over the existence of higher transactions costs associated with purchasing by fundholding practices (Dixon and Glennerster, 1995; Coulter, 1995a; Glennerster *et al.*, 1994a, 1994b; Petchey, 1993). Although no detailed studies have compared fundholding and HA transactions costs, it is clear that fundholders have set more complex contracts than HAs, often on a cost-per-case basis, requiring far greater time to collect information, to manage and to monitor on behalf of both the purchasers and providers. For example, a community trust estimated its costs in contracting with 13 fundholders for 4% of its income as four times higher per contract than the costs of its contract with the HA for 91% of its income (Audit Commission, 1996). Fundholding has also generated considerable costs in terms of the administration of the fund. It has been calculated that this cost can be up to one day per week for some GPs, potentially reducing the quality of primary care through a reduction in patient contact and the greater use of locums whose services also have to be paid for (Cornell, 1996).

Although high transactions costs appear to be recognised, they have, until recently, been unquantified. There have only been a few published estimates of the additional operating costs in certain localities. Pennington (1995), for example, crudely estimated the three-year operating costs of the Nottingham GP Commissioning Project at £3.9 million compared with an estimated £7.2 million for the fundholding equivalent. The Audit Commission's report found that the staff, equipment and computing costs of managing fundholding amounted to £232 million up to the end of 1994/95 (Audit Commission, 1996). The audited underspend for the same period, however, was only £206 million. Moreover, the estimated costs did not take into account the additional costs generated for providers and the additional GP time requirements for administering fundholding.

Financial management

It was noted in Chapter 3 that fundholders had generally made greater savings than HAs on their budget. In aggregate, they underspent on their budgets in each year from 1991 to 1996, compared with HAs who had initially underspent (but by less than fundholders), and then overspent in 1994/95 and 1995/96 (see Figure 3.1). However, it is unclear what the source of these differences was: the fundholder's ability to be a more efficient purchaser by being more economical in resource use or through obtaining lower prices from providers; or other factors such as a possible excess of funds allocated to fundholders, underbilling by providers; or lower demands for care in fundholding practices due to a more healthy practice population (Dixon and Glennerster, 1995).

There have been few studies investigating how fundholders have spent their savings. In a survey of 22 fundholding practices, the National Audit Office (1994) found that savings were used to enhance practice facilities, buy more staff and develop more in-house services. Set against this, there is anecdotal evidence to suggest that 'savings' may, on occasion, have been misused. Typical examples include the use of funds to purchase inappropriate non-patient services (Timmins, 1995a; Committee of Public Accounts, 1995) and to extend practice premises to increase the capital value of the practice to the benefit of the partners (Glennerster, 1994), although it can be argued that improved premises lead to better delivery of care. Moreover, only 17% of £111 million in audited underspends had been spent by the end of 1993/94 (Audit Commission, 1995b). Of these, 35% had been spent on improvements to practice premises, 25% on office and equipment supplies, 15% on medical equipment and, of the remaining 25%, only a proportion had been spent on extra hospital and in-house services. Thus, although savings were a definite by-product of fundholding, the evidence is unclear as to the source of the savings – and the efficiency with which fundholders used such savings is much debated.

Equity

Three major equity issues have arisen with respect to fundholding: access to care, 'cream-skimming' and budget allocation.

Access to care

On the introduction of the internal market, the most extensive predicted criticism of fundholding was that it would create a two-tier system of fundholding and non-fundholding practices. It was predicted that hospitals would give differential access to the patients of fundholders, particularly in cases where the fundholder could spend money on reducing waiting lists for elective surgery (Butler, 1992). It was also suggested that, if HAs failed to fund hospitals' work-rates adequately, elective surgery admissions for non-fundholders towards the end of the financial year would be restricted in favour of fundholding patients who could 'jump the queue' (Kingman, 1992).

In addition, it was argued that only the more advanced practices, with good support structures, would enter the scheme due to the high administration requirements of fundholding (Ham, 1991a). The scheme, therefore, would reinforce existing inequalities in health care by discriminating against small practices with fewer support staff which tend to be found in the more disadvantaged areas of big cities (Benzeval and Judge, 1991).

A plethora of anecdotal evidence for 'two-tierism' exists due to its inherent newsworthiness; reports were fuelled by comments from non-fundholding GPs, consultants, hospital managers and others (Milhil, 1993; Fisher, 1993; McCullough, 1993; Samuel, 1992; Luxton, 1993). A substantial review of anecdotal and opinion-survey evidence on access to care has highlighted a number of ways in which fundholders have been able to obtain advantageous terms of treatment for their patients (Association of Community Health Councils for England and Wales, 1994). In particular, fundholders have used their contracting power to obtain priority treatments for their patients in hospitals and to reduce waiting times for initial consultations. Moreover, fundholding patients have had better access to local outreach clinics taken at local GP surgeries. In addition, seasonal variations exist in access to hospital care because hospitals have admitted disproportionately more fundholding patients at the end of the financial year to maximise cost-per-case income once HA block volumes have been met. This increases the hospitals' incomes but means that patients are not being seen in order of clinical priority. Although the evidence presented is generated only from anecdote and from opinion surveys, the study concludes that there are strong reasons to believe that the patients of fundholding GPs have enjoyed better access to hospital treatment than other patients. These conclusions are backed up by an opinion survey of GPs in fundholding and non-fundholding practices carried out by the Consumers' Association (1995b).

However, research that has compared the referral rates and waiting times for patients in fundholding and non-fundholding practices provide evidence both for and against two-tierism. Research which suggests two-tierism includes a referral survey undertaken by South Bucks Community Health Council (1994). This survey revealed that patients of non-fundholders waiting for orthopaedic operations in the South Bucks Area waited on average 12 weeks longer than fundholders. Moreover, although there was no difference in the waiting times for operation in gynaecology, referrals for gynaecology appointments were longer for non-fundholding patients. These results, however, must be treated with caution because they are based on a very small sample of patients (54). A study based on 159,000 patients on referral rates to orthopaedic care by Kammerling and Kinnear (1996), however, also concluded that fundholding patients were seen more quickly than the patients of non-fundholders and that some hospitals had provided special clinics exclusively for fundholding patients.

A study on waiting lists in Oxford region by Peeke (1993) provided an alternative to the commonly held view. It concluded that there was no difference between the waiting times experienced by the patients of fundholders and non-fundholders in Oxford – contrary to the widely held beliefs of the local GPs. A study by Kind *et al.* (1992) also concluded that claims of a two-tier system seemed unjustifiable; both fundholding and non-fundholding GPs reported similar levels of difficulties with waiting times for hospital consultations. Similarly, the Audit Commission found that waiting lists for surgery had fallen in both fundholding and non-fundholding practices and did not differ significantly overall (Audit Commission, 1996). The Commission's methodology has, however, been severely criticised (Dowling, 1997).

The most recent evidence (Dowling, 1997), based on a database survey of 57,000 patients, confirms the existence of significant differences in waiting times. The research compared waiting times of fundholding and non-fundholding patients for elective surgery covered by the fundholding scheme at four providers over four years. It was found that the patients of fundholding practices had significantly shorter waiting times than those of non-fundholders for all four providers.

Overall, most commentators accept that fundholding has exacerbated two-tierism. Glennerster (1994), for example, whose commentary is broadly favourable to the scheme, suggests that the two-tier effect may be a transitional one, reducing as more GPs become fundholders. He suggests that as fundholders achieve improved services, much of that advantage will become available to some non-fundholding practices. For example, HAs may cannibalise aspects of fundholding contracts into their own and providers may find it easier and cheaper to provide a uniform service to all their GPs rather than just to fundholders. In the latter case, non-fundholders would receive spillover benefits. However, Glennerster concedes that the patients of non-fundholders are likely to become disadvantaged in the short term, resulting in an equity gap between the two kinds of patient. Glennerster's emphasis is on how to maximise the opportunities for spreading the benefits of fundholding to all practices, rather than a concern with abolishing the scheme to deal with temporary inequalities. It can be argued that the NHS has always been multi-tiered because the competence and energy of GPs varies.

Fundholding appears to have exposed previous differences and codified them into two tiers. The main argument is whether there can be a levelling-up process and whether non-fundholders can become successfully integrated into the scheme in some form.

A further equity concern was that the most knowledgeable and able individuals would be able to exert leverage on their GP whereas the least able would not. The work of Scott et al. (1996) has shown that socio-economic status does influence GP decision-making in that patients from higher social groups were more likely to be given a diagnostic test and less likely to receive a prescription. Although no study has examined whether fundholding would have the effect of exacerbating possible class gradients in access to care, the greater opportunity for patient choice and influence in fundholding practices does allow this possibility.

Cream-skimming

A major concern of analysts was the fear that the budget allocation to fundholders would be insufficient to cope with yearly variations and deviations in patterns of illness (Glennerster et al., 1994a, 1994b; Butler, 1992). Crump et al. (1991) estimated the financial effect of fundholding on practices with varying list sizes and concluded that volatile demand for services would have a significant impact on practices, particularly smaller ones, which would undermine the scheme. Indeed, Enthoven had suggested that fundholders would require a list size in excess of 100,000 to insure against risk, far higher than the proposed minimum size for a fundholding practice (May, 1989). Although a stop-loss arrangement was included for fundholding, so that the HA would become financially responsible for any individual case over £5,000 in one year, this did not protect against multiple admissions below this level or an unexpected rise in demand for care (Yule et al., 1994). As a result of these risk factors, some observers believed either that practices would be forced to pool savings as a safeguard for the future rather than spend them on practice improvements and patient care for which the money had been intended, or that they would indulge in extensive cream-skimming.

The danger of cream-skimming was a particular worry at the time of the scheme's introduction (Scheffler, 1989). Because practices would face the cost of treatment for the first time, they would have an incentive to discriminate against high-cost patients in favour of low-cost ones (Barr *et al.*, 1989). Moreover, evidence from the USA suggested that Health Maintenance Organisations, which were superficially similar to fundholders, did indulge in discrimination against poor (Ware, 1986), elderly and infirm people (Pauly, 1986; Petchey, 1997). As Brazier *et al.* (1990) suggested, because variations in health need can *never* be sufficiently accommodated into budgets, there will always be a range of health profiles from which to select. Many analysts, therefore, predicted extensive cream-skimming by fundholding practices.

Some authors claimed that cream-skimming has indeed occurred. Cornell (1996), for example, unequivocally states that 'a major drawback experienced by some patients is that they have either been refused registration with a particular GP or removed from a practice list on grounds of their illness being an expensive drain on the practice budget'. However, Cornell cites only the theoretical work of Crump *et al.* (1995) to substantiate this claim and provides no empirical evidence for the existence of cream-skimming. The Patient's Association, for example, has claimed that the removal of patients from GP lists is a growing trend in order to avoid excessive costs from seriously ill patients (*The Independent*, 1996). However, despite the allegations and the theoretical incentives, they present no cases in which fundholders have indulged in the process of cream-skimming.

The general view of the more sophisticated literature is that fundholders have not undertaken cream-skimming despite the theoretical financial incentives to do so. This may be due to a number of reasons including: generous budgets; the fact that GPs are not at personal financial risk; and, probably most important, the stop-loss insurance scheme by which the HA would pick up the bill for a particular patient if the cost exceeded a certain amount.

Budget allocation

At the beginning of the reforms, some analysts predicted problems with the fundholding budget allocation. Many believed that fundholders would be more generously funded to make the scheme a success – with an associated detrimental impact on funds in the HA. There was also a problem with the method of allocation. First, because fundholding budgets were to be set, at least initially, on the basis of historical levels of activity, past inefficiencies and inequalities inherent in the system would be 'legitimised' (Yule *et al.*, 1994). Second, the process would be open to abuse because greater activity levels recorded in the preparatory period would lead to higher allocations (Coulter, 1992). The inequities of the system led many observers to query whether there could ever be a fair system of funding (Dixon, 1994) as no manageable formula existed by which the needs of GPs' populations could be gauged (Paton, 1992).

A key question addressed in the empirical literature, therefore, was whether fundholders have gained a greater cash allocation than was their fair share relative to non-fundholders. The evidence for this is mixed. Dixon *et al.* (1994) suggested that fundholders received a higher than equitable allocation in North West Thames in the early stages of the scheme. They showed, for example, that the per capita funding for inpatients for non-fundholding practices varied from 59% to 87% of that for fundholding practices. Their work, however, was criticised for relying too heavily on the low quality routine data available and a series of 'tenuous' assumptions (Bowie and Sturgeon, 1994). Nevertheless, it is doubtful whether a better analysis of budget allocation could have been made with the data available.

That fundholders are better resourced is disputed by Glennerster (1994) who describes how national and regional comparisons do not suggest that fundholders have been more generously funded. Using figures for Regional Health Authorities, he shows that fundholders have not been over-funded because the application of the national average costs per capita for fundholding procedures suggests that fundholding practices are getting 15% less than expected. Moreover, Brogan (1993) points to a study in Oxford which showed that the budgetary allocation for fundholding practices was 9% less than the regional average. In the light of these figures, it is difficult to support the contention that fundholders have been systematically over-funded. However, the methodology employed in both these studies was not fully described, nor subjected to peer review.

Quality

In introducing the scheme, the Government believed that GP fundholding would motivate GPs to search for a better quality of hospital service. It was argued that poor care by hospitals would have a negative impact on the GP in terms of time and resources. Thus, giving the GP power to change provider would create leverage for change towards a better quality of service.

The ability of fundholders to channel savings back into the practice was seen as a major incentive of the scheme that would enhance primary care. It was believed that savings from budgets could be used to improve practice-based facilities and encourage the growth of outpatient clinics and on-site services more accessible to the GP population. Savings could also be used to buy more secondary care services and to clear waiting lists. Some analysts disagreed. They predicted that the quality of care in both the primary and secondary sectors would deteriorate. A particular concern was that the high administrative workload engendered might have a detrimental impact on the quality of primary care: reduction in patient consultation time and a fall in GP energy (Keeley, 1993). It was also predicted that the doctor–patient relationship would be threatened because the fundholding GP's role as patient advocate could become undermined by rationing responsibilities and the potential to make decisions based on financial rather than clinical grounds (Keeley, 1993; Francombe, 1991). The potential adverse impact on quality resulting from the budgetary impact on referrals and prescriptions has already been described above.

Another perceived danger to the overall quality of care stemming from the proposals for fundholding in the White Paper was a reduction in the effectiveness of planning services (Paton, 1992). The creation of fundholding would contribute to this decline in a number of ways. First, it was evident that if fundholding practices overspent due to unforeseen pressure for services, the onus would fall on the HA to bail them out (Secretaries of State for Health, 1989). The demarcation of a contingency reserve to insure against this problem would reduce HA flexibility. Second, top-slicing the HA budget would weaken HA responsibilities to plan health services in order to maximise health gain and address inequalities in provision (Butler, 1992; Keeley, 1993). Third, it was argued that fundholders would be poor purchasers because they did not have the skills or information necessary to make informed purchasing decisions (Atkinson, 1989). Moreover, because the purchasing decisions of fundholders would be uncontrolled the system would be inherently unstable (Ham, 1991a). Thus, the potential for substantially different purchasing priorities by GPs would undermine the strategic focus of the HA and could potentially frustrate the attainment of local health targets (Scheuer and Robinson, 1991). Finally, a reduced HA budget would increase financial shortfalls in hospitals and create the need for providers to 'sell' themselves to fundholders. In practice, this would reduce the ability of providers to plan services based on long-term stable demand (Paton, 1992).

The countervailing view was that fundholders would be far more effective purchasers than HAs because they could identify with the interests of the patient (Glennerster et al., 1994b). As Francombe (1991) reveals, one of the perceived advantages of fundholding was the promotion of the principle of meeting health need based on decisions about individual patients. Because GPs had first-hand experience, if not systematic knowledge, of both the needs of patients and the medical consequences of the treatment they received, purchasing would be far more effective than by a remote HA which purchased services through the use of population-based demand and assessment of need. It was also claimed that fundholders would be able to exert leverage on hospitals and improve quality, resulting in better relations with consultants, cost reduction, reduced waiting times and better specialist care (Benady and Barr, 1991). Fundholding was also seen as an opportunity to increase the responsiveness of hospitals, such as through more prompt discharge letters (Taylor, 1991). It was also suggested that HAs would respond to these benefits by improving quality specifications in their own contracts (Bowling et al., 1991).

The empirical evidence of the impact of fundholding on the quality of care provided falls into three categories: quality of secondary care provided; quality improvements in contracts with providers; and quality of practice-based services.

Quality of secondary care

Only two published studies have sought to assess the impact of fundholding on the quality of secondary care provided (Howie *et al.*, 1994, 1995b). The earlier of these examined the treatment of patients suffering joint pain in six Scottish fundholding practices before and after the introduction of fundholding. It found that the length of GP consultation and the prescription of pain-relieving drugs remained unchanged after fundholding came into effect while patients reported being less able to cope with their illness. In the more recent of these studies, which investigated a dozen conditions, including asthma, angina and diabetes, the conclusion was that the quality of care had been largely maintained. However, in some clinical areas, such as patients suffering with pain and patients with social and psychological problems, the quality of care appeared to have declined. That some groups of patients were less able to cope in fundholding practices raises a question about the sense of imposing an additional administrative burden on busy GPs at a time when patients' needs appear to becoming more complex (Coulter, 1995b). Ellwood (1997) found that while service quality issues were ranked by the majority of fundholders as the most important influence in their referral decision, it only very occasionally led to shifts between providers.

One limitation of the before-and-after analysis by Howie *et al.* was the lack of a control group of non-fundholders. This means caution must be taken in attributing to fundholding any observed changes in the quality of care, because no study has compared the experiences of fundholding and non-fundholding practices in this respect. Moreover, no work has directly investigated whether fundholding has improved the quality of clinical care provided by hospitals.

Quality improvements in contracts

The introduction of quality standards into contracts with providers has been shown to be a feature of both fundholders and district HAs (Coulter, 1995c). Studies which have investigated the impact fundholding has made to contracting have tended to be surveys of the views of fundholding GPs rather than detailed analyses of contracts. Nevertheless, all of these surveys reveal that fundholders were convinced that fundholding had been the catalyst to improved quality in contracts (Corney, 1994; McAvoy, 1993; Bain, 1992). These improvements appear to be in the area of organisational/process arrangements rather than the actual quality of clinical care. This is made clear by Glennerster *et al.* (1994a, 1994b) who cite examples of how fundholders used their purchasing power to improve information flows and engender a faster response rate to their referrals and requests for information. Other studies also agree that a change occurred in the power relationship between the fundholding GP and the provider; the most important benefit of this has been quicker and better communication links between fundholders and providers (Roland, 1991; National Audit Office, 1994; Cornell, 1996; McAvoy, 1993; Bain, 1992; Wisely, 1993). The main improvements for patients were reduced waiting lists and, in one case, improved courtesy.

The evidence on creating better quality services through contracts consists of descriptive case studies and anecdote. Although no study has sought to compare fundholding contracts with those negotiated by non-fundholders over the same period, there have been attempts to study the adoption and implementation of quality standards from the perspective of a GP multi-fund. Baeza and Calnan (1997), using a case study approach, showed that quality standards in contracts were derived and adopted with very little input from providers. The impact of these quality standards on hospital consultants' behaviour was negligible, there was very little monitoring of the standards by the multi-fund, and providers admitted accepting standards which they knew they could not meet. Furthermore, reports from non-fundholders involved in GP commissioning groups have made similar claims of improved standards through contracting (Black *et al.*, 1994; Eve and Hodgkin, 1991; Graffy and Williams, 1994; Corney, 1992; Willis, 1992). In the absence of a comparison between fundholding and non-fundholding practices, it is unclear whether fundholding has been the catalyst to these improvements or whether it is a general effect of the purchaser/provider split.

Quality of practice-based services

The use of fundholding 'savings' to enhance practice-based services and the ability through contracting to develop outreach clinics have been regarded as major benefits of the scheme. As the section on efficiency in fundholding showed, the evidence suggests that fundholders have been able to offer more on-site services and clinics than non-fundholders.

Although opinion surveys show that these initiatives are welcomed by patients who generally prefer treatment locally within familiar surroundings (Consumers' Association, 1995a), as discussed above there is some disagreement on whether the growth in on-site services necessarily leads to health improvement (Harris, 1997; King et al., 1994; Corney, 1992). Maynard and Bloor (1995) suggest that the popularity of enhanced local care has spread as a reaction to cost inflation in the hospital sector and because it has the advantage of being provided nearer to the community, is less technologically dominated and more user-friendly. However, they also warn that it may be 'unwise to recoil from an expensive, unproven hospital enterprise only to advocate increased resourcing and emphasis on another activity which is resource-intensive (particularly in pharmaceuticals) and also unproven'.

Overall, owing to the lack of empirical data on quality improvements in clinical care and the lack of any systematic comparison between fundholders, non-fundholders and other purchasers of care, it is impossible to show that the quality of care has improved through the introduction of fundholding. Except for the work of the Howie team, the evidence is mainly in the form of case study and anecdote, with most of the observed improvements being in terms of organisational changes rather than in terms of health outcomes.

Choice and responsiveness

An important ingredient in the reforms was the ability of the fundholding initiative to promote greater patient choice. Patients should have more power to influence the quality of services they received under the new system. This is because GP fundholders would be in competition for 'customers', and patients would be able to judge which practices offered the best service. As a result of this, the patient would have more choice in deciding at which hospital to receive treatment because GPs could respond to patient demand through their ability to exert leverage on providers. Furthermore, fundholding would be more responsive because it would be based on the GP's knowledge of patients' needs and experiences in a way which was impossible for an HA.

An important element in this argument was the ability of patients to make an effective choice between GP practices. However, some commentators believed that only the most knowledgeable and able individuals would be able to exert leverage on the GP (Glennerster *et al.*, 1994a, 1994b; Barr *et al.*, 1989). Thus, in the worst scenario, fundholding might have the effect of exacerbating the class gradient in access to care (Petchey, 1995). On the other hand, the mere fact that certain people might leave a practice does not necessarily mean that those left behind suffer a worse service. Indeed, the reverse is perhaps the more likely; a GP faced with a reduction in his or her list has a strong incentive to improve.

Whether patients of fundholders receive a greater choice of hospitals for their treatment has been measured through surveys of the views of GPs and patients. Mahon *et al.* (1994), for example, found that fundholding GPs reported: a greater willingness to take into account patients' preferences than non-fundholders; more willingness to refer patients greater distances for elective surgery; and a lower likelihood of considering only one hospital for a referral. On the other hand, patients of these GPs were unwilling to travel longer distances to be treated more quickly and most were indifferent to the issue of choice. This indifference is exemplified in another survey of patients which showed that 80% of patients did not know whether their practice was fundholding or not (Kind *et al.*, 1993b). Thus, whereas fundholders have reported greater willingness to offer patients more choice compared to non-fundholders, patients perceived that there was little difference in the level of patient choice. Moreover, a confounding factor to this research has been the 1990 GP contract which made it easier for patients to change doctor.

Studies of patient satisfaction are one way to get some insight into the impact of fundholding on responsiveness. Although there is evidence to suggest that satisfaction remains high in fundholding practices (Howie *et al.*, 1995a), patient surveys show that: the expectations of patients are rising (Armstrong *et al.*, 1991); patients of fundholders are significantly more critical of their GP than patients of non-fundholders (Consumers' Association, 1995b); and a reduction in patient–doctor trust has resulted (Marks, 1995). It has been suggested that this reduction in trust has come about as a result of the patient feeling that decisions made regarding treatment or referral are being undertaken on monetary rather than clinical grounds (Cornell, 1996). Alternatively, the observed growth in criticism may be related to the greater assertiveness of patients in the more affluent areas in which fundholding practices are located: patients' willingness and ability to express dissatisfaction is often related to socio-economic status.

There remains some difficulty with interpreting satisfaction surveys because there is a lack of comparison between fundholding and non-fundholding practices. Moreover, results from studies investigating patient choice are difficult to assess because they come from attitudinal surveys of patients and GP fundholders. From the patients' viewpoint, involvement in the choice of hospital has remained very low whereas satisfaction with the overall service received, irrespective of fundholding, has remained high. Thus there is no evidence of greater responsiveness to patients' views.

Accountability

Fundholding was intended to make the NHS more responsive to its users and be more businesslike (Wall, 1996). However, as power and resources are passed to the fundholder, the more the fundholder must, like any other spender of public funds, be made accountable for how budgets are spent. However, the lack of an appropriate accountability mechanism, both for the GP fundholders' use of underspends and for their purchasing decisions, was of increasingly widespread concern (NHS Executive, 1994a). Concern was also expressed over the lack of accountability of GP fundholders to patients (Association of Community Health Councils for England and Wales, 1995).

As a result, it has been generally regarded that accountability procedures within fundholding must improve. This problem was partially addressed by the Government through the launch of an accountability framework for GP fundholders in December 1994 (NHS Executive, 1994b) but, as the Audit Commission (1996) revealed, HAs had yet to develop explicit systems to judge how wisely fundholders are purchasing, or whether their purchasing represents good value for money.

Summary and conclusions

Although the evidence is in places controversial, it is probably safe to say that there is a reasonable degree of consensus on the following findings with respect to fundholding.

● The rise in prescribing costs was lower in fundholding practices compared with non-fundholding practices initially, but this differential appears to have been short-lived.

- There appears to be no difference in the increase in referral rates between fundholding and non-fundholding practices.

- There has been more practice-based care in fundholding practices than in non-fundholding practices.

- Providers have been more responsive to the demands of fundholders than non-fundholders.

- Fundholding has created a high administrative workload and high transactions costs for both purchasers and providers.

- There is a two-tier system in access to care; one for the patients of fundholders and one for non-fundholders.

- There has been little change in the level of patient choice.

While these are areas of consensus, the review of the fundholding literature also highlights a number of fundamental areas that have not been the focus for research. In particular, there is no evidence on whether fundholding makes a difference to the *quality* of primary or secondary care. Also, the true size of administration and transactions costs (particularly on providers) is unknown, which means that the real cost effectiveness of the scheme cannot be properly measured.

If this literature review was used to put GP fundholding on trial, it would be possible to form both a robust defence in favour of the scheme and to construct a viable prosecution against it. This is because of the equivocal nature of much of the evidence and, even where the effects are agreed, they can be interpreted as good or bad. For example, fundholders have generally shown greater capability for developing enhanced primary care facilities yet interpretations differ on whether this means better care or a more efficient use of resources than care provided in other settings. Similarly, while the literature supports the exacerbation of two-tierism as an outcome of fundholding, this has been interpreted in two ways. On the one hand it has been seen as a catalyst to the levelling-up of the quality of health care and a necessary interim product of the reforms

(Glennerster, 1994). On the other hand, two-tierism is interpreted as a major equity concern, benefiting the patients of affluent fundholders at the expense of smaller and less affluent practices – with poorer populations in greater need of care.

A further point to consider, which is fundamental to the evaluation of fundholding, concerns the characteristics of general practices themselves. The literature reveals, for example, that many non-fundholding practices have achieved efficiency improvements equal to, and better than, fundholding contemporaries. This greater efficiency may, therefore, be more likely to be a product of innovation in practices than the result of fundholding *per se*. Petchey (1995) supports this argument by citing work that revealed the existence of a stratum of 'innovator' practices before the existence of fundholding. Petchey goes on to argue that any superiority attributed to fundholding practices might be due to their status as 'innovators' rather than as fundholders. The report by the Audit Commission (1996) supports this by concluding that most fundholders are failing to secure the expected benefits for patients. Thus, while fundholding status appears to have given practices the increased potential for beneficial change, only certain innovative practices within fundholding have transformed patient care.

Differences in the abilities of fundholders to use their status to its best advantage suggest that, although fundholding has been an important catalyst for change, a wider set of variables exist. These explain why some fundholders appear to perform better than others and why some non-fundholders appear to be more innovative than some fundholders. The present Government's decision to wind up the fundholding scheme in 1999 in favour of Primary Care Groups, ostensibly because fundholding is both inequitable and costly to administer, could thus be missing the real issue raised from the experience of fundholding. This is not how costly or how inequitable the scheme has been, but how problematic it has proved for general practice to use fundholding at its innovative best. The issue to address, and one highly relevant to the arrangements for primary care envisaged in *The New NHS* (Secretary of State for Health, 1997), is how best to enfranchise general practice to take an active and innovative part within the health system.

5 Locality and GP commissioning

Jo-Ann Mulligan

It is clear that GP fundholding has received most of the attention as a mechanism for involving GPs in purchasing health services for their patients. However, a range of alternatives to fundholding emerged soon after 1991/92. At that time, HA managers and non-fundholding GPs began to seek ways to imitate the aspects of fundholding which looked appealing (such as GP input to purchasing decisions) and to avoid those aspects which they objected to (such as the alleged two-tierism of fundholding).

The term *'commissioning'* rather than *'purchasing'* was used to describe these schemes which operated below HA level and within the framework of HA purchasing (Mays and Dixon, 1996). The 'purchasing' undertaken by fundholders was defined by its critics as going out into the market place in the short term with a sum of money and buying from the range of services already on offer. 'Commissioning', by contrast, was defined by its proponents as working strategically with providers over a period of time to develop the desired pattern of local services without necessarily directly controlling the budget which would be used to purchase the services at the end of the process. Thus the wide range of different models of commissioning operated without budgets which had been allocated to them as of right.

Two broad types of commissioning can be distinguished principally by their origins (bottom-up versus top-down):

● *GP commissioning* in which groups of non-fundholding practices (although over time fundholders began to join in) come together in response to fundholding. They propose service changes and developments to the HA on behalf of their patients, which the HA incorporates into its contracts. In some instances, the GP commissioning group is given a notional or indicative capitation budget against which past activity and costs can be compared; this covers a range of the hospital and community health services previously purchased on the GPs' behalf by the HA. The range of GP involvement can include: practice visits; GP representatives on HA purchasing teams; GP–HA meetings and seminars; GP liaison managers; as well as forms of collective representation of GPs to the HA through local GP bodies (Exworthy, 1993b).

- *Locality commissioning* in which the HA brings together all the practices in a geographic area (typically an area with a population of 50–60,000). These form a group charged with eliciting the views of all the GPs in the locality and channelling these constructively into the HA's purchasing process. This is done either by influencing the plans of the HA directly or by working with local providers to agree changes which could then be incorporated in HA contracts. Whereas purchasing functions remain centralised, locality specific contracts can be set on the basis of locally determined needs and service development priorities. These groups normally have a paid coordinator from the HA.

In practice, the two types of scheme had much in common. They were collective, non-budget-holding alternatives to fundholding, working with or through the agency of the HA on behalf of a subpopulation of the authority. Both aimed to make HA purchasing more locally sensitive to variations in needs and patients' views, using GPs as the main source of information and to overcome the perceived remoteness of the HA bureaucracy. Both sorts of commissioning varied widely across the country in the details of how they were organised and their precise roles in relation to the HA. However, all relied heavily on their ability to *influence* local providers and the HA, without necessarily having the independent purchasing power to make their views count in the face of concerted opposition. In general, neither model included an incentive that any 'savings' created by cost-conscious purchasing could be retained by the group to spend on additional services or facilities.

Models of devolved commissioning have evolved rapidly and to varying extents across the UK. Smith *et al.* (1997b) have mapped the different approaches and found that most HAs had at least three different approaches to devolving responsibility for commissioning. Accordingly, a large number of evaluative studies have been conducted albeit of very variable quality. Most of the evidence reviewed here comes from those directly involved in the schemes; there have been few attempts to compare these approaches with either GP fundholding or other developments in HA-led purchasing. Moreover, none of the existing studies compare the outcomes of GP commissioning with those of HAs with poorly developed methods of involving GPs. Although, in view of the increasing convergence between models and overlapping participation by general practitioners, it would be difficult to control for confounding factors even if well-designed comparisons had been set up.

The vast majority of the research evidence has therefore focused on how the various models have evolved, rather than providing an absolute comparison with either the pre-reform state or other models of local purchasing. Among the case studies, descriptions and internal evaluations, there has been only one substantive attempt to compare the different ways in which GPs have become involved in purchasing (Glennerster *et al.*, 1996). The remaining literature has relied on evaluating individual models against internal criteria. Notwithstanding these criticisms, much can be learned from looking at the experiences of the various schemes described.

Efficiency

Two aspects of efficiency are considered: management costs and service efficiency.

Management costs

Possibly the best known GP commissioning scheme is documented by Black *et al.* (1994). A total of 200 non-fundholding GPs in and around Nottingham (representing at least 68% of the population) joined together to act in collaboration with their HA. The HA continued to hold the budget. The GPs reported that many of the benefits from GP fundholding – responsiveness, choice and quality – could be achieved without joining the fundholding scheme. The group were able to secure a large capital investment and reduce waiting times in three targeted specialties, yet estimated that its management costs were approximately half those of fundholders. Because the group did not even hold a shadow budget, the authors of the study believed that its success derived from its size, structure and rapid information dissemination. This meant they could show their providers that they had 'teeth' and could persuade the HA to take their business elsewhere if specified standards were not met. The group also took credit for the fact that Nottingham was the fifth most efficient teaching district in the UK in 1994/95.

In an unpublished evaluation of a GP commissioning scheme in Devon, Dixon et al. (1996) calculated that if all the GPs within their commissioning group had been fundholders then their management costs would have been £821,824 compared to the £25,000 they currently received from the HA. In common with all the studies reported here, the authors were able to discuss in general terms the various ways in which they had secured service improvements, but there was no attempt to relate them to the considerable indirect costs of negotiation and monitoring of service agreements.

A study by Balogh (1996) asked GPs and HA managers involved in commissioning to rate the effectiveness of different models for involving GPs in commissioning. The results indicated that GPs rated liaison with providers as the most effective model and practice-sensitive purchasing as the least effective. By contrast, managers rated project work and locality advisory groups the most effective model, but agreed that practice-sensitive purchasing was the least effective model. Although practice-sensitive purchasing might involve less commitment from GPs than GP fundholding, in terms of time and resources, these costs are likely to be higher than for locality purchasing because information on activity has to be broken down to a smaller level. Furthermore, other difficulties of the scheme include developing a practical and equitable method of practice resource allocation and ensuring that an adequate information infrastructure exists. Other anecdotal evidence (Murray, 1993) suggests that practice-sensitive purchasing is probably less efficient than most of the alternatives, but the structure does have the potential to produce some benefits. For example, the model has the advantage of being based around practices that, in contrast to fundholding, have the option to work together.

A different study (Hine and Bachmann, 1997) sought to describe the impact and direct costs of locality commissioning in Avon. The authors found that locality commissioning successfully changed services with limited extra funding and without delegation of hospital and community health service budgets. Costs mainly comprised the time of staff in primary care, secondary care and the HA. The local medical committee had spent £57,687 on locality commissioning, which amounted to 6p per capita. Although direct comparisons are not possible because most fundholders in the area also participated in locality commissioning, it does appear that the costs of locality commissioning compare favourably with those of standard fundholding and its extension, total purchasing. The Total Purchasing National Evaluation Team (1997) reported that the median costs of the first 'live' year of total purchasing was £2.77 per capita, whereas for standard fundholding the figure was £12.90 per capita over the first four years. However, the authors of the Avon study were not able to measure the effectiveness of each of the service changes that were implemented as a result of locality commissioning. Furthermore, only a limited range of costs were measured, reflecting the difficulty in identifying the indirect costs of, for example, support from providers and the HA.

Service efficiency

To be meaningful, efficiency must include some measure of benefits gained for a given cost. Pickin and Popay (1994) have argued that there appeared to be no obvious link between the level of costs and the benefits achieved in the locality commissioning schemes they studied. Although one might assume that costs will be greater than simple GP participation at the HA level, early anecdotal evidence suggested that locality schemes were still relatively 'efficient' (Ham, 1992a). One of the few detailed studies in this area (Office for Public Management, 1994) used a variety of sources of data (project documentation, financial schedules and minutes of meetings) to evaluate locality commissioning against specific criteria which included efficiency, responsiveness, quality and accountability. In terms of whether the project provided value for money, the authors found that it offered a cheaper administrative model than GP fundholding, mainly because it could draw upon the skills and expertise of the HA. However, although GPs had been involved in contract negotiations, what constituted that 'involvement' was harder to define.

Although not seeking explicitly to consider costs, Glennerster *et al.* (1996) did describe and evaluate the relative effectiveness of six schemes including: locality groups; provider purchasing; practice-sensitive purchasing; GP consultation groups; a district-wide GP commissioning executive; and a total purchasing scheme. They commented that, although the 'minimalist' schemes cost very little in administration, they had not made much impact compared with fundholding. They also found that the relative effectiveness of the models of involvement as perceived by the GPs themselves varied considerably, and concluded that the effectiveness of the various representative or locality schemes depended on how far HAs were prepared to act as GPs' agents. Crucially, where the HA took this role seriously, GPs stayed with the schemes. Where they did not, GPs moved into fundholding. Indeed, they concluded that the non-fundholding schemes that had had the most success looked most like fundholding. In other words, they gave GPs both autonomy and control. In the absence of information on cost-effectiveness a further important question for any scheme is the degree to which it is successful in achieving its own objectives. Glennerster *et al.* found that, compared with fundholders, locality commissioning groups were not as successful in solving the problems that they had identified for attention.

Willis (1996) reported brief results, in terms of service efficiency, from four GP commissioning groups around the country. One group in Northamptonshire, by negotiating direct access to same-day ultrasonography for patients, claimed that they had greatly improved the service while reducing the number of patients admitted by over 50%, so producing financial savings. Further money was saved by direct access to a tonsillectomy list. Research undertaken by the Primary Care Support Force in London (1996) claimed that GP involvement in the commissioning process ended unnecessary duplication of some services. The Nottingham non-fundholders reported prescribing costs 7% lower than the national average (Nottingham Non-Fundholders, 1996). In Devon, Dixon *et al.* (1996) showed that when negotiation with providers failed to improve waiting times, the group demonstrated that they had 'teeth' by putting providers on notice stating that they intended to remove contracts at full cost unless targets had been achieved or action plans agreed. Service specifications were negotiated directly with consultants, and trust managers' studies showed that improvements had been achieved. These examples indicate that, when pushed, some GP-led groups can achieve a degree of change. However, the evidence is mostly descriptive and it is still not clear whether these groups are more, or even at least as, efficient as fundholders.

Equity

Both locality and GP commissioning have been envisaged as ways of overcoming the two-tierism associated with fundholding by involving all GPs to help shape health services. The benefits can then be enjoyed by the whole population. The mission statement of the Nottingham non-fundholders' group is typical:

> To ensure the purchasing of quality secondary care which is equitably available to the patients of all general practitioners, and to co-operate in this endeavour with all interested bodies.
> (Black et al., 1994)

Within the context of the Nottingham non-fundholders, this meant guaranteeing equity of access to a trust's services by negotiating explicit statements into the contract together with appropriate penalties for transgression. A considerable amount of anecdotal and hard evidence appears to point to inequities in the fundholding model but, although the pursuit of equity is often stated as a clear intent for non-fundholding schemes, its execution seems to be more often assumed than explicitly measured. We could identify no studies that compared waiting times, referral rates or access to specialist services for fundholding schemes with alternative devolved models of purchasing. In terms of access to services, many GP commissioning groups cite that service improvements are available to all patients not just to those belonging to their particular group and that, by default, this promotes equity (Glennerster et al., 1996; Dixon et al., 1996; Nottingham Non-Fundholders, 1996). For example, Glennerster et al. reported that, although fundholding GPs and GPs taking part in locality commissioning schemes shared the same criticisms of services, the latter group were more reluctant to seek changes without doing so for the whole area, giving equity considerations as a reason. This suggests clear differences in motivation and in priorities between GPs in different fundholding groups and those participating in locality commissioning schemes.

Quality

Two aspects of quality are discussed: the quality of health services and the quality of GP involvement.

Quality of health services

A prime incentive for GPs to get involved in devolved purchasing is the hope that the quality of health services can be improved. One GP commissioning scheme in Hackney was able to demonstrate positive findings in relation to this (Graffy and Williams, 1994). The Hackney scheme is similar in many ways to the Nottingham non-fundholders group (Black *et al.*, 1994) where a single GP forum works to influence health services. Graffy and Williams examined the minutes of meetings of a GP forum and the contract between the HA and the main provider to determine whether the forum had had an impact on service developments. They found that not only did most GPs and managers feel that the forum was representative, but that 55% of service developments had originated from the GPs. As in the Nottingham scheme, the local context was crucial; relatively few GPs within the Borough were fundholders and this made it easier for them to gain credibility with providers. The authors of the Devon study (Dixon *et al.*, 1996) concluded that the most important achievement from the perspective of local GPs was a reduction in waiting times for all patients in the area. Moreover, the authors claimed that fundholders in the same area had been unable to bring about such changes. Research based on two locality schemes in Newcastle and County Durham (Smith and Shapiro, 1996) also found that there had been achievements in terms of both service changes and the development of new relationships and alliances.

Glennerster *et al.* (1996) considered how far each of the six schemes in their study had helped GPs achieve the changes they sought in four different specialties. The authors found that fundholders not only identified more problems with local services, but also were more successful in achieving improvements than locality or GP commissioning groups (68% success rate versus 40% for non-fundholders). However, there are some confounding factors, not least the differential financial support given to fundholding as opposed to non-fundholders. Proponents of non-fundholding claim that their results would be different if they had equivalent support. Furthermore, locality commissioning groups were much more reluctant to seek changes if these did not or could not accrue to the whole area. On the other hand, fundholders were not obliged to address area-wide issues of concern and this might explain their higher success rates. Glennerster *et al.* concluded that, if locality and wider commissioning were to work, then they would need significantly more administrative resources.

The Avon locality commissioning scheme in Hine and Bachmann's study (1997) identified 20 initiatives which had changed services to patients. The commonest initiatives concerned: primary mental health care; nurse specialists for primary care of chronic diseases; referral and clinical practice guidelines; and access to hospital outpatient departments. In their discussion, the authors point out that most new projects arose when additional funding became available rather than from moving existing money. Furthermore, high-cost hospital services rarely encountered by GPs did not feature. The authors suggested that this selective approach could reflect the early stage of development, limited financial support, or the preference of GPs to concentrate only on certain issues. The latter conclusion supports findings from the national evaluation of total purchasing (Total Purchasing National Evaluation Team, 1997) where all participating practices focused only on selected issues, at least in the first year of 'live' purchasing.

Experience from a locality commissioning scheme in Northumberland has been mixed (Balogh and Thomasson, 1995). The local HA decided that local suggestions for service enhancement would be incorporated as locally sensitive variations in contracts. Many of these mirrored services which fundholders had negotiated in different parts of the county. However, the authors pessimistically concluded that:

> ... *pressures over agreeing contracts for 1995–96 ... will inevitably mean that the locality GPs' lists of priorities may remain unfulfilled.* (Balogh and Thomasson, 1995)

These 'pressures' were unspecified but the quote highlights the fear that unless additional resources for management of locality commissioning groups are made available there is a danger that change will only be marginal.

Jankowski *et al*. (1997) reported brief results from a locality commissioning scheme in southwest London. They surveyed the elected lead GPs in 15 localities, members of the GP commissioning executive and HA link staff working with GPs in localities. The authors found that most of the benefits reported from the scheme were in primary care and community services, such as improvements in physiotherapy services and the redistribution of midwives according to need rather than historical practice. Both GPs and HA staff agreed that locality commissioning 'would lead to many benefits'. The authors also found a significant degree of variation in how GPs wanted different models to be developed in the future to achieve improvements in services. Some wanted to manage real budgets whereas others wanted to have more of an advisory role to the HA.

Quality of GP involvement

Research by the Primary Care Support Force (1996) also explored the extent to which GPs were involved in making decisions about commissioning. Their survey asked both GPs and managers to assess the extent to which GPs were involved in a decision-making or advisory capacity. The majority of GPs (81%) considered their role to be advisory, whereas only 39% felt they had a role in making decisions. This result contrasted with the managers, of whom almost equal numbers considered GPs to be involved in making decisions and giving advice. The authors noted that comments throughout the questionnaire completed by GPs reflected a general feeling that their advice was taken only if it agreed with the HA view.

The British Medical Association (1997) surveyed local medical committees (LMCs) and HAs to determine the extent and nature of GP involvement in the commissioning process. Not surprisingly, the study found that a plurality of structures existed by which HAs elicited GP participation. In terms of the effectiveness of that participation, 69% of respondents from LMCs believed that the advice they gave was taken into consideration by HAs. This figure was considerably higher than for HA respondents (45%) suggesting that GPs might be more positive about the impact they felt they were lending to the commissioning process.

Another dimension of quality concerns the extent to which different purchasers encourage the Health Service to develop new techniques or new models of service delivery. The London Health Economics Consortium (1996) reviewed the published and unpublished literature and found that GP involvement as a whole had an important effect on innovation, although it was not clear how far fundholding or other models of GP-led commissioning were the 'defining influence' on this. Significantly, the authors concluded that the influence of GPs on innovation is quite specific and that it does not usually include a mechanism for making strategic innovations without the coordination of a third party such as the HA.

Choice and responsiveness

The evidence on consumer choice is limited and mixed. Unlike fundholding, there have been few surveys of patients to measure consumer satisfaction. In some respects, one could argue that the goals of choice and responsiveness were not necessarily prime objectives of these schemes in the way that they were under the introduction of the fundholding system. But, as the section on fundholding showed, the idea of patients smoothly switching from one GP fundholder to another in order to get the best service didn't happen in practice. In theory, GPs in non-fundholding commissioning groups should be able to exploit their clinical knowledge to act as a patient advocate to improve local health services in much the same way that fundholders have claimed to have done. There is certainly some indirect evidence which suggests that GP commissioning groups are responsive to local health care needs and many groups pride themselves on this aspect. The Hackney GP forum (Graffy and Williams, 1994) surveyed its GPs and found that 74% agreed that the forum was effective at influencing the health service locally. However, research by the Primary Care Support Force (1996) indicated that more progress may need to be made in this area. GPs who were involved in the commissioning process (n = 93) were asked a series of questions on the effectiveness of their involvement in seven aspects of commissioning, two of which were responsiveness to local people and relationships with local alliances. Less than a third believed that their involvement was effective in either of these areas. Furthermore, both areas received the lowest rating out of the seven aspects of commissioning considered (the other aspects were: strategy, effective contracts; knowledge base; relations with providers; and organisational capacity). This is clearly important given that GPs are close to their patients and are supposed to have a detailed understanding of their needs. The authors concluded by warning of the danger of using the views of GPs as proxies for the views of service users or the public, because their priorities for health care do not always coincide.

Many locality commissioning schemes have also hoped to demonstrate various benefits such as changes in responsiveness to views of local people (Ham, 1992b; Layzell, 1994) but again existing evidence of how effective this has been is limited. In Newcastle and North Tyneside (Smith and Shapiro, 1997) there is some evidence of schemes seeking the views of local patients in planning services. Participants in one scheme thought that, on the whole, localities were an appropriate vehicle for engaging local people in assessment and prioritisation of health needs. Freake et al.(1997) reported on the success of an initiative, also in Newcastle, which involved the appointment of a researcher to undertake interviews with primary care workers and over 50 local community groups. The groups had the opportunity to raise concerns not only about Health Service issues, but also about the wider issues of community consultation and future participation. Importantly, the groups were able to arrive at a consensus on three priority areas for future work and these were noticeably different from priorities defined by other localities. However, improved sensitivity to local needs and requirements can also encourage wide variations in the extent and location of services. In the same way as fundholding, policy makers will need to be clear how these variations can be justified within a national service.

Accountability

As noted in the fundholding chapter, a frequent criticism of GP fundholding is the perceived lack of accountability of GPs to the centre for their purchasing decisions. Mays and Dixon (1996) have suggested that developing effective means of making devolved purchasers accountable for their decisions in general poses a major problem for the NHS. Unfortunately, there is little evidence concerning the accountability arrangements for GP or locality commissioning and none to suggest that it is any more or less than for fundholding or locality commissioning. Two forms of accountability are considered here: accountability to the HA; and accountability to the GPs that the commissioners are supposed to represent.

Accountability to the health authority

A study of locality commissioning in London by the Office for Public Management (1994) found that accountability arrangements had proved unsatisfactory to a certain degree. The process by which the GPs were held to account was not made explicit until GPs sought to act differently from the approach recommended by the HA. Significantly, tensions then arose around the different interpretation of the terms 'accountable' and 'devolution', because the HA had not spelled out how the devolution of decision-making would work in practice.

A simulation exercise, also organised by the Office for Public Management (Crail, 1997), attempted to model the impact of locality commissioning over two years using the experience of one HA. The results proved worrying in terms of public accountability. Without a strong planning framework, the participants found there was a danger that conflicting commissioning local decisions would act against the public or patient interest. This was exacerbated by the fact that the locality teams pursued largely independent agendas and ignored policy decisions being taken at the HA. The net effect was confusion about the roles and responsibilities of the HA and the new locality boards and little exchange of information between localities. Another unforeseen consequence was the conflict of interest for GPs between their roles as commissioners and providers because the exercise resulted in the closure of a large acute hospital leaving GPs with no local maternity, accident and emergency (A&E) department or emergency admissions service. An obvious caveat to interpreting these findings is that this was a simulation exercise and, as such, the effects are exaggerated as participants 'drive' the system to some logical end-point. Nevertheless, it still reveals the potential dilemma in engaging GPs in a process which can lead to their involvement in making quite difficult decisions. This has even more relevance in the context of the primary care groups outlined in *The New NHS*.

Accountability to GPs

To what extent are GP and locality commissioning groups accountable to those they claim to represent? The Primary Care Support Force (1996) explored this issue in detail in its survey of GPs involved in commissioning. The study looked at the method of selection to a commissioning group, which gives an indication of to whom GPs were accountable. Of GPs, 39% had been nominated by a GP forum and 32% by a Local Medical Committee, with 25% joining at the invitation of the HA. Because representation of a defined constituency is one way of achieving accountability, a number of HAs had arrangements for election of GP representatives by GPs on a geographical basis. However, there was ambivalence about how far HAs should pursue a 'gold standard' level of representation; GPs felt it was more important that feedback to other GPs occurred. However, although 96% of GP respondents consulted colleagues, most of the consultation was reported as 'informal'. In some cases this meant using GP fora and practice meetings. Only 18% of the GPs used formal methods such as surveys, newsletters and circulation of minutes. In their survey, Graffy and Williams (1994) also asked GPs whether a GP forum represented their views well. A total of 90% said it definitely or probably did. In addition, 89% of the health service managers agreed with the related statement: 'the GP forum is representative of local GPs'. This suggests that different models of GP commissioning are achieving some success in terms of peer accountability.

Summary and conclusions

The evidence for locality and GP commissioning can be summarised as follows.

- Estimates for transactions costs are lower than under GP fundholding but these estimates do not include negotiation time and other costs.

- There have been improvements in services but probably not to the same extent as those claimed from fundholding.

- There appears to be greater scope for promoting equity compared to fundholding.

- There is some limited evidence of peer accountability to GPs.

- Many schemes have shown an improvement in GP–HA relations.

Although the evidence on locality and GP commissioning is not strong, there are valuable lessons to be learned from it. This is because such schemes tended to operate somewhere between the extremes of single practice fundholding and large population-based HA purchasing in terms both of scale and degree of direct budgetary control at local level. One of the key questions is whether it is possible to make the same sorts of quality and efficiency gains as were reported under fundholding, but at lower cost because of the absence of devolved budgets to manage and separate contracts to negotiate. Stand-alone studies of individual initiatives tended to conclude that it is possible (Willis, 1996), but the only study which attempted in any way to compare commissioning with fundholding came to a less favourable conclusion (Glennerster *et al.*, 1996).

It is apparent that much of the success of these schemes depends on the local context and on the attitude of the HA. Shapiro *et al.* (1996) concluded that the form and style of HA leadership seemed to be vital to the nurturing of effective relationships in the commissioning process. In many respects the working together of the HA, GPs and locality managers was the most commonly cited benefit to date, by both GPs and the HA (Smith *et al.*, 1997a). Yet, as highlighted in Chapter 4, to what extent are the GPs who join these schemes typical of GPs as a whole? In other words, what or who are we evaluating – an effective scheme or a particularly effective group of GPs?

Notwithstanding the above, in terms of contributing to the *strategic* objectives of commissioning, locality and GP commissioning groups do seem better placed to make an impact than GP fundholding and, when allowed to be selective in approach (rather like standard fundholding), they can make a difference to the quality of services. However, they appear to be less successful than GP fundholders in negotiating with providers, and the true costs of such groups are still largely unknown. What is clear is that the concept of GPs being involved in the commissioning process (in whatever form) is now so embedded in the NHS that the uncertainty has moved from whether they should be involved to finding ways of extending current approaches to GPs who currently have little or no involvement.

6 Total purchasing

Nicholas Mays and Jo-Ann Mulligan

Total purchasing is possibly the most significant development in NHS purchasing of health services since the introduction of GP fundholding. The national total purchasing pilot (TPP) initiative was introduced by the NHS Executive in 1994 following bottom-up local initiatives by ambitious fundholders in pioneer projects. Under total purchasing, volunteer standard fundholding practices, either alone or in groups, are delegated a budget by their local HA to purchase potentially all of the hospital and community health services not included in standard fundholding for their populations. At the same time as the TPPs were introduced, the NHS Executive also announced the setting up of a series of extended fundholding pilots (EFHs). In these, standard fundholding practices took responsibility for purchasing an additional area of service beyond fundholding, such as maternity, inpatient mental health services and specified complementary therapies such as osteopathy and chiropractic.

The EFHs and TPPs are three-year experiments. Total purchasing is seen as a development of GP-led purchasing, but in cooperation with the HA; the total purchasing budget remains the ultimate responsibility of the HA, projects are typically set up as subcommittees of the HA, and HA staff support them. The rationale for the introduction of total purchasing appears to have been that fundholding GPs would continue to innovate as they had under standard fundholding and would develop new and more sensitive ways of meeting patients' needs than their parent HAs. For example, they might substitute primary for secondary care because, unlike ordinary fundholders, TPPs have no incentive for shifting costs to budgets which are the responsibility of the HA. Total purchasing was seen simply as the next step in the national evaluation of fundholding.

Unlike standard fundholding, the NHS Executive's first-wave ($n = 53$) and second-wave TPPs ($n = 34$) and maternity and mental health EFHs ($n = 9$) are the subject of an extensive three-year national evaluation in England and Scotland. The study is the first Government-funded evaluation of a major initiative resulting from the NHS and the Community Care Act, 1990 (Total Purchasing National Evaluation Team, 1997). The research methods include a mixture of quantitative and qualitative methods and the findings presented here are based largely on an interim report (Mays *et al.*, 1998a) , supporting working papers and a summary of the principal findings to date from the programme of research prepared for the Department of Health and NHS Executive at the end of October 1997. The national evaluation final report is due at the end of 1998. In addition, we identified three other smaller scale evaluations of a single TPP in Berkshire (Walsh *et al.*, 1997), a single TPP in West Yorkshire (Harrison, 1997b), and a primary-care-led extended purchasing project very similar to the official TPPs in Doncaster (Newbronner, 1996). These had all reported initial findings, at the time of writing. Other evaluations of individual projects were in progress but had not been reported.

It is still very early for a thorough assessment of the potential of total purchasing because the first wave of national pilots only completed its first 'live' year of purchasing at the end of March 1997. However, the quality of the evidence already available is easily superior to that of locality commissioning or GP-led commissioning. There is, of course, far less evidence than accorded to standard fundholding.

The scheme has been implemented without a central blueprint and minimal guidance, partly because of strong conviction from the centre that GPs had great potential to improve the efficiency of services through their purchasing and that they should be allowed as much flexibility in implementation as suited local circumstances. Hence, as shown for locality and GP-led commissioning in Chapter 5, there is considerable variation between TPPs. This 'hands-off' approach has presented considerable difficulties in assessing whether the projects have been successful because the objectives of total purchasing as a national scheme were never spelled out in detail. For example, TPPs are free to choose which service areas they wish to work on. As a consequence, total purchasing might be better relabelled '*selective purchasing*' because none of the TPPs is currently purchasing all the hospital and community health services for its enrolled population. In addition, about 30% of the 53 first-wave TPPs did not even take control of a budget in 1996/97

(Robinson *et al.*, 1998), suggesting that not all the TPPs could have been described strictly as 'purchasers' in the first year! On the other hand, almost half of the lead GPs at first-wave TPPs reported that there were straightforward arrangements in place for the project to retain any 'savings' from its budget to reinvest in further services, thus creating a clear incentive for economical behaviour (Total Purchasing National Evaluation Team, 1997).

At present, the scheme appears to represent an amalgam of standard fundholding, GP commissioning, locality commissioning and joint HA–GP purchasing (co-purchasing) activities with the emphasis varying between projects. Some projects have not yet taken budgets and have no independent contracts whereas others have a number of contracts that include large amounts of secondary care expenditure. Some TPPs have focused their efforts on purchasing services such as maternity and emergency inpatient services which are new to GP-led purchasing. Others have used their TPP status and budgets to concentrate on developing primary care services, including many services already included within the standard fundholding scheme.

Structurally, the first-wave TPPs vary widely. Of the original 53, 16 were single-practice projects and 37 were multi-practice projects. The average population was 33,000, ranging from 12,000 to 85,000 patients. There was an average of 3.6 practices per project, ranging from one to ten practices. At HA level, TPPs accounted for between 2% and 20% of the HA population. The management arrangements have also varied considerably because the vast majority of the single-practice projects have operated without a dedicated project manager; the opposite has been the case in the multi-practice projects where managers have been appointed in the vast majority of cases. In addition, the projects differ in the complexity of their managerial arrangements. The larger TPPs tend to have a separate project board which is the subcommittee of the HA, an executive board which makes the day-to-day decisions and originates the strategy of the TPP, together with a range of permanent and ad hoc subgroups responsible for specific aspects of total purchasing (Total Purchasing National Evaluation Team, 1997).

Efficiency

Two efficiency issues are considered: management costs and service efficiency.

Management costs

Walsh *et al.* (1997) in their evaluation of the Berkshire Integrated Purchasing Project, one of four pioneer TPPs which preceded the first wave of national pilots, compared HA management costs with those of the project. They warned, however, that such comparisons are fraught with difficulties (and these apply to all comparisons with the HA) because of:

- the statutory obligations of HAs which are not shared by TPPs and which can occupy varying amounts of staff time;

- additional work at HAs as the local health services arm of central government for many purposes;

- different packages of service purchased (TPPs have 'blocked back' certain services to the HA as selective purchasers);

- HAs now include the functions of the former Family Health Services Authorities (FHSAs) in relation to planning primary care services and monitoring prescribing; and

- the fact that the management costs of TPPs, unlike fundholding, are negotiated from the overall management budget of the HA.

There are clearly many other differences that make comparisons problematic. Initial findings from Berkshire suggest, however, that total purchasing is more costly than fundholding because it is, in many ways, a more ambitious scheme, which may also be reflected in higher transactions costs.

The direct management costs of running the first-wave TPPs have varied widely. In their preparatory year (at 1996/97 prices) they ranged from £7,500 to £84,000 (median £37,500) per year for single-practice projects and from £5,100 to £339,000 (median £100,000) for multi-practice projects. This reflects the diversity in scale, scope, ambition and managerial infrastructure of the TPPs. The median cost for all TPPs in 1995/96 was £67,000 and in the following year it was £58,000. The equivalent per capita figures for all TPPs were from £0.11 to £7.49 in the preparatory year of 1995/96 with a median of £2.78. The direct management costs associated with total purchasing in the first live year (1996/97) also varied widely amongst the projects (Posnett et al., 1998). The management cost data show that larger TPPs, not surprisingly, are more costly in total to manage because of the need to establish a managerial identity separate from individual practices, but that multi-practice TPPs are no more costly to manage per capita than single-practice projects. The 34 TPPs in the second wave had lower management costs in their preparatory year than the first wave, both in absolute and per capita terms. This is largely attributable to the higher proportion of small multi-practice TPPs and a few much larger multi-practice TPPs in this group.

Data from the national evaluation of TPPs indicate that the highest performing TPPs in the first live year, as defined in terms of their reported achievements, had considerably higher management costs than the lowest performing projects. Projects with higher levels of ambition for future purchasing in 1997/98 were also more likely to have higher management costs, suggesting that the level of investment in management infrastructure was associated in some way with the effectiveness of the pilot project (Mays et al., 1998b). Higher-spending TPPs tended to receive additional funds (to pay not only for locum cover for their lead and for other GPs to take part in the scheme, but also frequently an allowance for each GP or practice). This suggests that the range and depth of GP involvement may be one source of better performance.

Because the costs of devolved forms of purchasing have shown few signs of directly reducing HA management costs, the relative cost of TPP and HA purchasing and their combined cost to the NHS in the presence of standard fundholding have important policy implications. A study by Griffiths (1996) based on 11 HAs and nine GP purchasers (six fundholders and three TPPs) in three regions in 1996/97 produced an average total management cost per capita of £9.93 for the HAs, £4.60 for standard fundholders and £7.02 for TPPs; this included their fundholding costs (i.e. a marginal cost over fundholding of £2.40 which is very similar to the average of £2.82 reported in the national evaluation of total purchasing (Posnett et al., 1998). It is possible that the total costs of purchasing/commissioning could, therefore, be as high as £17 per head of population, assuming little or no substitution between the different forms of purchasing. Using data from Griffiths (1996) and the national evaluation of TPPs, it is possible to estimate the *purchasing* costs of the HA in order to compare them directly with the purchasing costs of GP-led purchasing, including total purchasing and standard fundholding. The comparison indicates that even with a move to more collective forms of GP-led purchasing such as TPPs, the costs are likely to be greater than if purchasing were to remain with the HA. There is little evidence that management costs per capita for TPPs decline as they get larger, although there are fewer over 50,000 population. Therefore the policy issue may turn on the ability of the different approaches to bring about efficiency improvements in services.

Despite the concerns of providers that TPPs would generate considerable additional costs for them, early findings from the national evaluation of first-wave TPPs suggest that the full transactions costs of total purchasing (as against the direct management costs at project level) in the first live year have fallen disproportionately on the projects themselves, particularly on the leading GPs involved (Posnett et al., 1998). Total transactions costs thus correlated closely with the management allowance negotiated between the TPP and its host HA. The marginal transactions costs of total purchasing over standard fundholding at the eight TPPs studied in detail varied between £1.43 and £4.11 per capita in 1996/97, suggesting that it is difficult to generalise about the additional costs of TPPs. For some acute providers, the presence of a TPP *reduced* its transactions costs of negotiation with local fundholding practices. In general, the costs of contract specification and negotiation were lower in the presence of a TPP than had been the case under standard fundholding alone, suggesting that there are some economies of scale in dealing with larger purchasing entities. The additional costs generated by total purchasing for the health system as a whole were largely associated with activities such as general coordination and information gathering, which would remain even if the internal market and contracting were abolished. For example, time and effort is required to reach a consensus between a group of GPs on potentially sensitive issues such as rationing resources or using clinical protocols (Harrison, 1997b).

Service efficiency

Reflecting the early stage of these projects, there is only limited evidence about the progress that has been made towards service efficiency objectives. The authors of the Berkshire Integrated Purchasing Project evaluation sum up by commenting:

> *Our overall assessment at the end of the first live year is that the project group has spent a lot of time setting up new systems and not so much time focusing on the project objectives.*
> (Walsh et al., 1997)

In terms of reducing inpatient admissions, data from the Berkshire Integrated Purchasing Project showed that there was no significant difference in the number of emergency admissions for the TPP compared with non-TPP practices locally. Similarly, there were no significant differences in average length of stay. The analysis of changes in hospital activity between 1995/96 and 1996/97 for first-wave TPPs in the national evaluation was still incomplete at the time of writing due to HA delays in providing data. However, early analysis of data on six of the nine TPPs which had explicit objectives to reduce acute lengths of stay and/or admissions indicates the *potential* of TPPs to alter patterns of hospital use (Mays et al., 1998a; Raftery and McLeod, 1998). Four TPPs achieved their main objectives in relation to acute hospital utilisation and two had made some progress.

A typical example of a success was a TPP which had aimed to reduce total activity at its main acute provider by 10% by early discharge of elderly patients to a new rehabilitation facility at the local community hospital. The TPP succeeded in reducing its number of occupied bed days for medicine and surgery by 10.7% at the acute hospital. Average length of stay fell from 15.9 days in 1995/96 to 10.9 days in 1996/97 compared with 16.2 days and 15.6 days, respectively, for local non-TPP practices sharing the same main provider. Although a substantial volume of work was transferred to the community hospital, the daily cost of the rehabilitation beds was lower than that charged by the main acute provider. Another successful TPP reduced acute admissions by increasing the resources of a local hospital-at-home scheme whereas local non-TPP practices saw an *increase* of their admissions. Because the subsample analysed to date included the first-wave TPPs most likely from their purchasing objectives for 1996/97 to have made changes in their use of acute hospital services, these findings show the *potential* of selected total purchasers to influence the use of beds rather than the impact of a representative group of TPPs. It is likely that TPPs without independent contracts will have made fewer changes.

Although direct data on the overall efficiency implications of these changes in bed use are not yet available, it does appear that the TPPs are able to reduce activity at higher-cost providers and increase it at lower-cost providers. However, in system-wide efficiency terms, much will depend on whether or not overall treatment rates rise, fall, or stay the same. It will also depend on whether the acute hospitals are able to reduce their running costs commensurate with their reduced activity levels so that resources are genuinely released rather than costs passed onto other purchasers. In the absence of comparable routine activity data in all types of hospitals and in primary care, it is impossible to tell whether any TPPs have been able to purchase a greater volume of care for the same resources than their local HAs and, in turn, impossible to say whether this represents an efficiency gain. All that can be confidently said at this stage is that TPPs can successfully take initiatives designed to reduce or improve the efficiency of hospital spending.

Although not directly relevant to service efficiency, data are available from the national evaluation of TPPs on the reported ability of the TPPs to bring about their purchasing objectives in 1996/97 by service area. In general, the evidence suggests that the projects were motivated to attempt to bring about change by the GPs' perceptions of local problems rather than a strategic assessment of patients' service requirements. A considerable number were devoted to maintaining local acute services when these were threatened by centralisation plans (Harrison, 1997b). In addition, many of the objectives of the TPPs were couched in general or process terms (e.g. provision of high quality care as locally as possible, or increasing GP influence over purchasing decisions) making it difficult to assess their consequences.

First-wave projects reported having achieved about half of their main objectives in the first live year (very few TPPs achieved all their four main purchasing objectives).They tended to be more effective in altering and developing primary and community health services than in bringing about change in the way secondary care providers operated, especially in the case of mental health services. For example, although TPPs reported achieving 82% of their objectives in relation to developing the primary care team or services in primary care, they reported achieving only 33% of their mental health objectives and 41% of their objectives in relation to altering the way in which emergency medical care was provided (Mays et al., 1998b). In part, these first-year findings indicate the time required to bring about service change in more complex service areas, particularly when national policy does not provide a straightforward framework for GP action (e.g. in mental health where there is a tension between specialist agencies targeting the most severely ill and GPs increasing provision in primary care to those with less severe problems – see Gask et al., 1998). The difficulties encountered in realising objectives in relation to secondary care were also caused by a widespread, although not universal, difficulty which TPPs faced in releasing resources from the hospital sector due to overwhelming pressure on the acute sector from rising emergency admissions (Harrison, 1997b; Mays et al., 1998a).

Equity

On the whole, studies of total purchasing have devoted little attention to equity, either as an objective or as a consequence of projects. This is at least partly due to the overriding task of getting the projects off the ground operationally. However, the Primary Care 2000 project evaluation in Doncaster (Newbronner, 1996) did ask GPs and HA managers about 'cream-skimming'. In particular, they were asked whether working to a budgetary limit might affect the GPs' clinical decisions or deter them from accepting potentially expensive patients onto their lists. None of the GPs felt that working to a budgetary limit would actually affect whether they treated a patient who was in real need. However, they did recognise that it might affect how or where the patient was treated. Neither the GPs nor the HA contributors believed there was any real danger of potentially expensive patients not being accepted onto a GP's list. The main reason for this was ethical, but there were also practical considerations too. As all GPs in PC2000 were relatively close together geographically, it is likely that if a patient were turned away from one practice they would simply end up on the list of another PC2000 GP. In this respect, total purchasing is like locality commissioning and might have greater scope for promoting equity than standard fundholding.

Similar questions were asked of GPs, project managers and HA staff in the preparatory period as part of the national evaluation of first- and second-wave TPPs. As in the Doncaster study, the respondents consistently stated that cream-skimming and related forms of unfair treatment of more costly patients were not likely to be problems in total purchasing. In part, this may have been because the TPPs were *selective* purchasers and did not have full financial responsibility for all the needs of their patients. In part, this response may have been based on a judgement of the political reality that if a patient were known to be being denied urgent treatment on cost grounds by a TPP, the Service would have to over-spend and bail the TPP out in order to pay for the patient. It may also have been a reflection of the relative generosity of the TPP budgets.

An important aspect of equity in relation to total purchasing, as for other forms of devolved purchasing, lies in the way in which the TPPs' service budgets are set. Budget-setting was the most contentious issue in the preparatory period for the projects and remained a major problem for the second wave. Most HAs with TPPs have used a mixture of capitation and historical activity and costs to estimate budgets. The proportion of TPPs funded simply on the basis of past spending has tended to reduce with time. The difficulty of disentangling TPP population expenditure from the rest of the HA's expenditure and delays in setting budgets for specific service areas involved in total purchasing, mean that it has not yet been possible to assess the relative resource levels of TPPs and their parent HAs as part of the national evaluation of TPPs.

Quality

Although most practices entered total purchasing to enhance the quality of service provision, we know very little as to whether services have actually been improved. This is compounded by the fact that HAs do not investigate the appropriateness of services purchased by TPPs. Only six out of 45 HAs with first-wave TPPs mentioned that they would monitor quality standards (Dixon *et al.*, 1998). Instead, monitoring and audit is dominated by accounting concerns and rarely appropriateness or value-for-money. The national evaluation uncovered only one HA that mentioned the possibility that there might be standards against which the performance of GP-led purchasers could be assessed, although they could not actually name any!

An indirect means of assessing the *potential* for TPPs to bring about quality improvements is to study the extent to which they use research evidence to guide their purchasing objectives. The national evaluation of TPPs has shown that poor activity and cost data hamper many TPPs' attempts to change services (Mahon *et al.*, 1998). In addition, although most TPPs report an understanding of the importance of using evidence from research on the effectiveness and cost-effectiveness of treatment to support service development and purchasing, few are using evidence in any substantial way. The main input to purchasing decisions is the GPs' own knowledge based on experience of the problems and limitations of the local health system.

Choice and responsiveness

Relatively little information currently exists about the impact of fundholding or total purchasing on responsiveness to patients. In their evaluation of the Berkshire Integrated Purchasing Project, Walsh *et al.* (1997) examined the following:

- what patients knew about fundholding, total purchasing and other related organisational changes within primary care;
- whether patients in these practices experience higher levels of satisfaction than patients in non-fundholding practices; and
- the impact of total purchasing on patient choice and involvement.

The patient questionnaire (n = 715) found that satisfaction with all aspects of care was higher among patients from the TPP practices than from comparison practices. Furthermore, 51% of TPP patients compared with 35% of non-fundholding patients agreed that they were given enough choice by their GPs about the different kinds of treatment and resources available. However, few patients had noticed any new or different services over this period. Significantly, a large majority of patients from both TPP and comparison practices wanted more involvement in practice decisions, particularly those related to service changes.

The national TPP evaluation reported that, although some TPPs were consulting the public before changing services (albeit, in a limited way through practice meetings and leaflets, etc.), most were more reluctant, stating that, as GPs, they already had a good idea about what their patients wanted (Dixon *et al.*, 1998). Many consulted the local Community Health Council (CHC) in some way and a few TPPs had CHC representatives on their project boards. TPPs reported similar difficulties to HAs in developing effective dialogue with their patients and/or the local public (Harrison, 1997b; Mays *et al.*, 1998a). However, it was clear that consulting and involving patients was not a high priority, at least not in the first two years of the first-wave projects.

The evaluation team for the Berkshire Integrated Purchasing Project argued that there was clear scope for the project to develop the level of patient involvement further as there were no current requirements placed upon GPs to account for their purchasing decisions to their patients.

Accountability

Two forms of accountability are considered: managerial accountability and financial accountability.

Managerial accountability

Although GPs are directly allocating resources, the HA still has overall responsibility for the deployment of those resources under the current arrangements for total purchasing. The national evaluation of TPPs identified a 'loose, informal framework of accountability' (Dixon *et al.*, 1998). HAs seemed reluctant to hold TPPs to account more formally. In many ways, the fact that each TPP is effectively a subcommittee of the HA (in contrast to fundholding) makes it convenient for the HA to monitor the TPP less explicitly, given other priorities. This might also have reflected a desire not to antagonise the GPs, particularly in the early days of the scheme, together with the deliberately *laissez-faire* manner in which total purchasing as a pilot initiative was introduced by the NHS Executive. An interview survey of regional fundholding and total purchasing lead managers at each of the English Regional Offices of the NHS Executive was undertaken at the end of the preparatory year for the first-wave projects. It showed clearly that Regional Offices were adopting a 'hands off' policy regarding the TPPs. They were relying on their normal performance management relationship with the parent HA on the grounds that, viewed externally, the TPPs were indistinguishable in accountability terms from their host HAs because their budgets remained the responsibility of the authorities (Strawderman *et al.*, 1996). In fact, many HAs, in their turn, appeared to be not only unwilling to hold the TPPs to account more rigorously using explicit criteria, but also did not appear to have the capacity. However, the evaluation team for the Berkshire Integrated Purchasing Project (Walsh *et al.*, 1997) argued that *local* accountability among GPs and between the practices and the HA had been strengthened as new forms of organisation had been formed, linking general practices with one another and to the HA.

The accountability arrangements for TPPs and their successor primary care groups (PCGs) will require further development, given that both schemes entail the delegation of many millions of pounds of public money and a substantial potential to shape the development of local health services to groups of independent contractors.

Financial accountability

Conventional financial accountability has received far more emphasis because TPPs are responsible for more NHS funds than standard fundholders. GPs can act as both purchasers and providers, raising the possibility of conflicts of interest (Mays and Dixon, 1996). It is therefore important for them to avoid such accusations. The national evaluation showed that monitoring of financial performance occurred regularly (monthly or quarterly) through meetings of the project board (Dixon *et al.*, 1998). Typical activities included monitoring expenditure and activity against budget, attempting to explain variances and encouraging the TPP to take action to avoid overspends. In the first live year (1996/97), most of the projects were able to keep their spending within budget, though only a third had agreed protocols for modifying spending to stay within budget (Bevan *et al.*, 1998). However, there was practically no activity by HAs to query the rationale for, or appropriateness of expenditure on, specific NHS services. For example, only six out of 45 HA managers mentioned monitoring the quality of services purchased by TPPs and none gave specific details.

Summary and conclusions

The evidence as it relates to total purchasing can be summarised as follows.

- TPPs vary greatly in size, management arrangements, objectives, whether they have budgets and their reported achievements in 1996/97. All are, in fact, *selective* purchasers.

- In general, total purchasing appears more costly to run than standard fundholding, primarily because it is more ambitious. It has added to NHS costs. However, the direct management costs of running the first-wave TPPs varied widely. The TPPs which reported a higher level of achievement had higher management costs in the first year of purchasing.

- There is limited evidence on whether TPPs have achieved service efficiency objectives, but projects have shown the potential to alter the use of acute hospital services both in terms of admissions and bed days. They have reported being able to achieve about half of their self-defined objectives. They have found it difficult to shift resources out of acute hospitals because of the increased demand for such services across the country.

- Although studies of total purchasing have devoted little attention to equity, total purchasing probably has greater scope for promoting equity than standard fundholding. This is because many TPPs are collectives of practices, but it will depend upon the precise way in which TPP budgets are negotiated with the host HA.

- Although improving the quality of services is almost always the stated objective of TPPs, we still know very little about whether the quality of services has improved under total purchasing. Most TPPs did not formally assess their patients' needs or systematically use research evidence to inform their service specifications.

- There has been little emphasis on accountability considerations other than ensuring financial accountability. TPPs have not given high priority to informing or involving their patients in their purchasing decisions.

Because the resources deployed by TPPs are delegated to them by their parent HA and remain the ultimate responsibility of the HA, total purchasing is, essentially, a GP-led collaborative venture with the HA. Thus it is not possible to compare TPPs as purchasers with HAs in any straightforward way. Originally, TPPs have much in common with GP-led commissioning groups and those TPPs which had not yet taken a budget in 1996/97 were also very similar in resource management terms. In essence, TPPs seem to be hybrids, lying between the practice partnership and the HA bureaucracy (Harrison, 1997b). However, the most interesting aspect of TPPs lies in the fact that they represent, albeit on a smaller scale, a dress rehearsal for elements of the Labour Government's proposed system of primary care groups (PCGs) which will commission hospitals and community health services for larger populations of about 100,000 people. The TPPs evaluated in this chapter are closest to the so-called 'level 2' PCGs outlined in the White Paper of December 1997 (Secretary of State for Health, 1997). The larger scale of PCGs poses a major organisational development task (see Chapter 9 for details of the PCG scheme). The evidence on TPPs indicates that the more successful PCGs will need to:

- recruit highly skilled managers and put in place good information systems which will not be compatible with significant reductions in local NHS management costs;

- develop a new form of organisation linking a larger number of previously independent GPs, including ways of taking strategic decisions and managing cash-limited budgets in common;

- retain the capacity to negotiate their own independent contracts with providers;

- develop mature, long-term relations with the local HA and local providers while reserving the right to move resources away from existing providers if necessary.

The interim report of the national evaluation of total purchasing discusses the implications for PCGs in greater detail than there is space for here (Mays *et al.*, 1998b).

7 Trusts

Richard Hamblin

Within six years of the creation of the internal market all providers of NHS health care in the United Kingdom had become NHS trusts. These are self-governing organisations, such as hospitals or groups of hospitals with the exclusive responsibility of providing services. However, NHS trusts have attracted little research attention compared with the purchasing side of the internal market. Furthermore, the available evidence is of variable quality, with the majority of studies being at the lower end of the hierarchy set out in Chapter 2. Why is this so?

One explanation, as stated in Chapter 1, is that the then Secretary of State, Kenneth Clarke, was reluctant to allow evaluation of the NHS reforms. Clearly, this reluctance did not stop a far larger amount of research on GP fundholding (see Chapter 4), but the comparative independence of GPs meant that they could decide whether or not to be studied. Trusts were very much part of a new system, directly accountable to the Secretary of State. Indeed, the reforms made providers *more* accountable to the Secretary of State; they had previously been part of HAs which were, in turn, accountable to the Regional Health Authority. It was, therefore, much less likely that a trust would allow access to data in order to be evaluated, particularly when the Secretary of State had effectively discouraged their cooperation in research.

Another explanation is that the pattern of development of trusts turned out to be unfavourable to rigorous studies comparing them with similar non-trust providers, known as directly managed units (DMUs). The first wave of trusts (1991/92) was restrained from making major changes to the provision of services, since the first year of the internal market was planned as a so-called 'steady state' in which purchasers contracted for historical, pre-reorganisation, levels of activity. The second wave (1992/93) was dogged by political uncertainty, because there was a general election within a week of their inception with both opposition parties committed to the abolition of the internal market. In both cases, research was difficult. By the time the third wave of trusts emerged, the numbers of DMUs remaining were too small and too atypical to offer an effective comparison.

A further explanation is the absence of real competition following the introduction of trusts. *Working for Patients* (Secretaries of State for Health, 1989) sets out a series of improvements which were expected to follow from the introduction of trust status. These accord to four of our five criteria for evaluation: efficiency; quality; choice and responsiveness; and accountability. The first three were seen as the inevitable result of the introduction of competition into the NHS, whereas the last can be seen as a part of the intention to 'create a stronger sense of local ownership and pride'. There is no mention of equity.

The belief that the introduction of competition into the NHS would lead to greater efficiency, quality, choice and responsiveness was part of the 'wider Conservative policy of reshaping the public sector that has consciously drawn on the private sector for ideas' (Harrison, 1993). However, it is questionable whether real competition was ever introduced. Prior to the introduction of the NHS reforms, some expressed doubts that competition could be achieved for the majority of hospitals in the country which are outside conurbations. Because competition was seen as the key to achieving these improvements, it is not surprising that little evidence of them taking place has been uncovered.

Most of the evidence presented here consists of anecdotal and indirect research. The exception is for efficiency, where a number of more rigorous studies have taken place. As in the other chapters, the five criteria of *efficiency, equity, quality, choice and responsiveness* and *accountability*, are used to structure the presentation of the evidence.

Efficiency

The expectation of increased efficiency in NHS trusts is explicit in *Working for Patients*, and it is clear that this was expected to result from the introduction of competition into the NHS. It was also apparent in the Government's belief that the supposed greater managerial autonomy associated with trust status would enable better, more business-like management to be pursued, resulting in greater efficiency. There are a number of inter-related ways in which trusts could become more efficient: through reducing their unit costs; through introducing more cost-efficient techniques; by responding to the demands of a more stringent financial regime; and by increasing the amount of activity carried out with the same resources. Critics of the reforms such as Moonie and Galbraith (1989) argued that trusts would actually be *less* efficient than DMUs because the internal market would require a new bureaucracy to service it (for example, departments to negotiate and monitor contracts), thus increasing transactions costs. We consider unit costs, financial regime, cost-efficient techniques, increased activity and transactions costs in turn.

Unit costs

Bartlett and Le Grand (1992, 1994a, 1994b) found some evidence that trusts had lower costs than DMUs, but noted that first-wave hospitals appeared to be a self-selected group which had had lower than average costs before becoming trusts. They therefore concluded that claims that the better performance of trusts was due to the reforms must be treated with caution. Second-wave trusts showed slightly lower costs than DMUs, but the authors argued that this was probably due to their case mix, size, patient flow and location rather than inherently better management performance.

The view that first-wave trusts had lower costs prior to the reforms has since been challenged by Söderlund *et al.* (1997), who argued that when variation in case mix is included in the analysis, 'costs decreased significantly with the change from directly managed to trust status'. They conceded that it was possible that hospitals were intentionally less productive before becoming trusts so that large gains could be shown on changing status. They also found evidence that hospitals which already had effective cost control mechanisms in place might have been more likely to have become trusts, so some of the productivity gains might have happened irrespective of trust status.

The balance of the evidence suggests that, although the early waves of trusts appeared to have lower unit costs than the remaining DMUs, it is far from clear that trust status was the cause.

Financial regime

The expectation that the new financial regime of trusts would increase their efficiency once their capital assets ceased to be treated as a 'free good' has been challenged by Shaoul (1996) on three grounds. First, Shaoul questions the relevance of applying charges for the use of capital, arguing that this is a surprising route to efficiency when less than 10% of all health expenditure is on capital. In contrast, pharmaceutical prescriptions, which make up a greater proportion of total NHS expenditure, are governed by an agreement with the pharmaceutical industry, the Pharmaceutical Price Regulation Scheme, which allows pharmaceutical companies to make a generous 20% return on their capital. Furthermore, Shaoul challenges the assumption that, because capital was a 'free good' before 1991, it led the NHS to be wasteful and inefficient in its use. Shaoul argued that comparisons with the private health sector are meaningless because private hospitals can 'cherry-pick' treatments that maximise their incomes. Shaoul also argued that if NHS hospitals are to appear as 'efficient' as private hospitals under these terms 'The implication for the NHS is that the hospitals must also throw off the shackles of socially necessary service provision in order to meet their financial obligations'. This would have a negative effect on both quality of service and equality of access. Moreover, charging for capital has negative effects for choice, equity and quality. Hospitals which had difficulty meeting what Shaoul regarded as inappropriate statutory financial targets would have to reconfigure and/or merge. This usually requires the closure of services which can reduce quality, ease of access to care and patient choice.

Another criticism of the financial regime for trusts was that the rules contained numerous perverse incentives which punished so-called more 'efficient units'. Adams (1995) outlined the case of the Oxford department of neurosurgery, the acronym of which (OxDONS) had become synonymous with these problems. In particular, he argued that money did not 'follow the patient' as was envisaged in the White Paper. Furthermore, the requirement that 'prices have to follow cost' (the demand for a 3% efficiency gain each year) and the demand that private income be used for revenue, not capital funding, led to the financial demise of the unit. On the basis of this analysis, he argued that 'efficient' in Health Service terms is, in fact, a euphemism for 'under-resourced'.

Efficient techniques

The increased freedom that trusts were to enjoy, combined with the demand for increased efficiency, led to expectations that trusts would be in the vanguard of introducing more efficient clinical techniques. Smee (1995) analysed the implementation of day surgery (supposedly a more cost-effective mode of treatment for some conditions that require elective surgery) in first- and second-wave trusts compared to DMUs and special health authorities (SHAs). He found a far from straightforward picture. First-wave trusts did have higher rates of day surgery than DMUs, but second-wave trusts had lower rates. Both waves of trusts had lower rates than the SHAs, but the evidence did not suggest that trusts were more efficient than DMUs.

Increased activity

Increased activity carried out by trusts has often been presented as an increase in efficiency. Department of Health figures have repeatedly shown an increase in trusts' activity as measured by the cost-weighted activity index or CWAI (NHS Management Executive, 1991; NHS Executive, 1994c, 1995). However, the assertion that this represents an increase in efficiency has been challenged on a number of grounds.

The Radical Statistics Health Group (1992b) has argued that the increase in finished consultant episodes (FCEs) which underlies the CWAI has been misleadingly interpreted as an increase in the number of individual patients treated. In fact, the increase in the number of FCEs between 1990/91 and 1992/93 was almost entirely due to the number of episodes lasting up to one day. They concluded that this increase could not be attributed unequivocally to the internal market, rather it was likely to have been caused by changes in medical technology. A similar argument can be made that at least part of the increase in FCEs was due to an increase in serial admissions, namely patients having a high number of short stays in hospital rather than one long one, due to changes in clinical practice.

Furthermore, the change from patient episodes to FCEs as a measure of activity just before the reforms (1988/89) makes it difficult to judge whether an increase in the numbers of FCEs is part of a longer-term trend or a result of the internal market. A new FCE is initiated each time a patient is referred to another consultant within the same hospital episode. This is further complicated because the use of the FCE has a tendency to inflate activity levels. This issue has been well rehearsed by a number of researchers (Seng *et al.*, 1993; Clark and McKee, 1992; Garrett, 1996; Harrison *et al.*, 1995). The ratio of FCEs to hospital stays has grown since the introduction of the internal market. This suggests that hospitals are paying increased attention to recording all transfers made by patients between specialists within the hospital during a single episode of care. This phenomenon further complicates any attempt to measure true increases in activity. One can only conclude that the evidence attributing increases in activity to trust status is at best unsafe.

Transactions costs

Critics of the reforms claimed that trusts were likely to lower the level of efficiency because the costs of managing the purchaser/provider split would increase their costs and those of the purchaser. Any possible reduction in unit costs of services would have been more than offset by increases in the transactions costs required by the contracting (Wall, 1994; Moonie and Galbraith, 1989).

Evidence frequently cited for this is an increase in the number of managers, which is seen as diverting funds unproductively from patient care. However, the evidence is not easy to interpret. Although the number of senior managers in the NHS increased by 10,000 between 1991 and 1994, it is not clear how much of this increase can be attributed to the introduction of trusts. The Conservative Government's explanations for the increase in the number of managers since the reforms included the claim that most of the increase had been due to the reclassification of senior nursing, health professional and administrative staff as managers and necessary strengthening of administrative functions (e.g. personnel management) rather than additional bureaucracy to support the reforms themselves (Government Statistical Service, 1994, 1995). Appleby (1995) also points out that the absolute increase in the number of NHS senior managers between 1987 and 1991 (that is, before the reforms) was as great as the increase between 1991 and 1994.

Further analysis of this issue is provided in the Audit Commission's *A Price on Their Heads* (1995a) which discussed the complex issue of how management costs should be calculated and, in particular, which staff should be counted as managers. The Audit Commission argued that the cost of *managers* was calculable, but that this was not to be equated with the cost of *management*, citing the example of one trust where 11 out of 62 staff classified as 'managers' had primarily clinical roles.

The evidence that trusts have increased efficiency is therefore at best inconclusive. Even where studies have shown trusts with lower unit costs, it is difficult to prove that this was due to trust status *per se* rather than any other factor. Neither does routine monitoring of activity imply that trusts have been more efficient than DMUs. Similarly, claims that trusts have directly contributed to observed increases in activity in the NHS are questionable. Contemporaneous changes in medical practice have had a significant effect on the number of FCEs – a measure that is not without its own problems as it may 'inflate' the apparent activity of a trust. On the other hand, claims that trusts have been responsible for a decline in efficiency through increasing management costs are equally unproven.

As increased efficiency was expected to follow the introduction of competition and self-management, the difficulty in proving that trusts increased efficiency in the NHS may be linked to the lack of competition between them. In theory, competition between hospitals should have been possible. The likelihood of competition was studied by Appleby *et al.* (1994) who concluded that, in at least one region, the conditions existed for competition between most acute hospitals in the NHS in 1991/92. Similarly, Propper (1995a) estimated that only 8% of the sample of acute service providers had a monopoly of general surgery, orthopaedics, ENT and gynaecology inside a 30-mile radius. In other words, 92% of these acute trusts were in a *contestable* market for these services.

However, actual competition and contestability are distinct. The lack of local monopolies (however local is defined) may point towards a 'contestable' market, yet genuine competition may have been impossible at the time of the reforms. In arguing for the necessity of regulation of the internal market, Propper (1995b) pointed out that instead of a competitive market, what resulted was a series of bilateral monopolies between purchasers and providers.

Equity

Working for Patients made no claim that trusts would increase equity in the NHS. However, their introduction held the *potential* to threaten equity in two ways. First, as Shiell (1992) suggested, trusts could choose to 'cream-skim' – i.e. only offer those services which guaranteed the highest income-to-expenditure ratio rather than provide the services that the local population needed – or refuse to offer costly treatments. This would mean that patients in some parts of the country would not be able to receive treatment available elsewhere. Second, they could have 'two-tier' relationships with their purchasers – favouring some (GP fundholders) over others (HAs).

Cream-skimming

There is little evidence on cream-skimming. The issue of withdrawing expensive treatments seems more a problem produced by allowing purchasers to have discretion over setting priorities, the most notable example being the case of 'Child B' suffering from leukaemia. A more widespread, but less newsworthy, example is the varied availability of beta-interferon for multiple sclerosis sufferers in different areas of the country.

Two-tierism

The position regarding the second potential source of inequity is less certain. Although there is little systematic research, there is much anecdotal evidence that trusts have adopted, or have considered adopting, a differential access policy between the patients of GP fundholders and non-fundholders. The ease with which fundholders can change the provider with whom they contract for a service compared with larger HAs may act as an incentive for trusts to have differential access policies to ensure that waiting times for fundholders are lower and that they will, therefore, not be tempted to remove a contract.

The Association of Community Health Councils for England and Wales (1994) chronicled 23 separate alleged examples of trusts admitting patients more rapidly if they were referred by fundholders. It may be that some of these examples were instances of HAs completing their elective contracts early in the year whereas fundholders had not. Yet if this was the case, it highlights that a systemic source of inequity in the internal market was instituted, with fundholders able to 'ring-fence' their elective work because they did not need to purchase emergency care. Significantly, there was a common perception that trusts treated fundholders more favourably than HAs. Francombe (1996), surveying a sample of London doctors, found that 88% of the sample believed that fundholders were treated differently by trusts. Further evidence is discussed in Chapter 4.

Quality

Working for Patients (Secretaries of State for Health, 1989) saw competition between individual trusts and DMUs as a force for improving the quality of the services provided. Paragraph 1.9.(ii) is explicit:

> ... [trusts] will have an incentive to attract patients, so they will make sure that the service they offer is what their patients want. And in turn they will stimulate other hospitals to respond to what people want locally.

In contrast, Wall (1994) expressed concern that the continuity of patient care could be adversely affected by conflicts of interests between different types of trust. For example, acute trusts would have an incentive to discharge patients as early as they possibly could; whereas community trusts would have incentives to prevent acute trusts doing this.

The effect of trusts on the quality of patient care is difficult to measure. One could, for example, present individual case studies of clinical advances and service improvements made at trust hospitals following the reforms as evidence of the success of trusts in this area. However, there are two compelling reasons for rejecting this approach. First, advances in the quality of care in hospitals have been made both before and after the introduction of the NHS reforms, and in both trusts and DMUs. Second, it is hard to see how quality improvements could be attributed uncontroversially to trust status alone. Thus, we make no attempt to present case studies of service improvements in NHS trusts as evidence of increased quality. Rather we seek more substantial evidence of quality improvement. This falls into three categories: attempts to review the quality of services in trusts, particularly in comparison with DMUs;

consideration of the effect on the continuity of care of dividing health services' provision between a number of separate trusts; and the question of waiting times for elective treatment.

Systematic studies of quality

There appears to be little evidence comparing the quality of care in trusts with the quality in DMUs. Furthermore, there are no before-and-after studies. Jones *et al.* (1994) looked at the quality of care of elderly people during the early stages of the reforms. Unfortunately their study took place inside an entirely non-trust environment. The survey of Directors of Public Health reported by Marks (1995) showed that most felt that the introduction of trusts had led to an improvement in services rather than a deterioration.

More compelling evidence on the effect of trusts on quality derives from the Clinical Standards Advisory Group (CSAG) (1993a–e, 1994a–d, 1995a–c). The CSAG was created, in response to medical criticism of the reforms, to provide an independent source of expert advice to health ministers and the NHS on standards of clinical care and access to services experienced by NHS patients. Yet, the extent to which CSAG reports consider the effect of trusts, and indeed any aspects of the internal market, is limited. Some of the reports do not even make a distinction between trusts and DMUs. For example, the report on back pain used data prior to the reforms and the report on schizophrenia notes only that 'good' providers and purchasers tend to be found together. On the other hand, the report on emergency admissions compared the performance of trusts and DMUs and found that DMUs generally admitted patients slightly more quickly through accident and emergency (A&E) departments than trusts did. However, the report also found that whether a hospital was a trust or not had far less impact on the time between arrival at the A&E department and admission to a ward than the referral source (i.e. 999 or GP-referred), the condition of the patient, the specialty to which the patient was admitted, and whether the hospital was a single-site or multi-site unit. In a number of CSAG reports, clinicians also expressed concern that quality of care for specialist services would suffer because purchasers would make choices based on price rather than clinical judgement. However, no evidence of this happening was presented in these reports. As an assertion, it is more commonly considered to be an effect of purchasers' behaviour rather than that of trusts.

Continuity of care

As Wall (1994) has pointed out, acute and community trusts potentially had conflicting incentives which threatened the quality of continuing care. Muijen and Ford (1996) have further elaborated this theory for mental health. They argued that trusts, health purchasers and local authorities all had different incentives concerning the provision of care for patients with mental health problems. This led to the development of integrated community care for seriously mentally ill people being undermined at a time when everyone was demanding its improvement. Strong evidence of the poor quality of working across boundaries was produced by the King's Fund London Commission (Johnson et al., 1997; Warnes, 1997). However, this was concentrated particularly on the boundaries between health services, social services and housing departments rather than between different types of trust.

Waiting times

Just as activity increases have been claimed as increases in efficiency and, in turn, attributed to the effect of trusts, so the Conservative Government claimed that reductions in waiting times were an improvement in quality attributable to effective trust operation. Indeed, reducing waiting times could be said to have been the central priority of the Government's acute hospital policy in the mid-1990s. The average length of time spent waiting undoubtedly decreased since the introduction of the reforms, and it has been claimed that the reforms themselves, rather than increases in overall funding and in the priority given to waiting list cases, were responsible.

However, these claims can be questioned for two reasons. First, the various waiting time initiatives predated the NHS reforms, having started in April 1987, two years before *Working for Patients* and four years before the establishment of first-wave trusts. Thus, the attempt to reduce waiting times for elective procedures, and importantly the funding associated with it, were distinct from the 'Working for Patient' reforms.

Any success of the waiting time initiative may be just that, the success of a specific policy with specific funding, rather than a product of the internal market.

If the latter had been true, one would have expected to find that trusts reduced their waiting times more quickly than DMUs in the early years of the reforms. Smee's figures questioned this (Smee, 1995). The percentage of patients waiting over one year fell between 1991 and 1993 at trusts and DMUs alike, yet the rate of decline was faster in DMUs than in second-wave trusts. Similarly, the total numbers waiting increased at both trusts and DMUs, yet the figures rose nearly twice as quickly at second-wave trusts than at DMUs. It is not clear that trusts were instrumental in reducing these waits. These data also exemplify how hard it was to make trust/DMU comparisons in such a changing situation.

Overall, there is no systematic evidence that trust status has, of itself, increased the quality of care for patients as was expected in the White Paper. Indeed, the lack of evidence of the effect of trusts on quality of care is of note and concern. It can also be argued that the structure of the purchaser/provider split, combined with separate acute and community trusts, had the potential, at least, to disrupt the continuity of care.

Choice and responsiveness

Working for Patients saw increased patient choice as essential to improving the efficiency and quality of health services. However, there is little empirical evidence of increased patient choice created by trusts. To consider the effect of NHS trusts on patient choice, it is necessary to ask whether trusts were even capable of increasing choice.

There are two convincing *a priori* arguments as to why trusts were unlikely to have increased choice. The first has been made by Propper (1995a), who pointed out that trusts did not offer choices directly to patients, but to purchasers, whether HAs or GP fundholders. The effects of this were shown in the study of whether the conditions for competition were present in the West Midlands by Appleby *et al.* (1994).

They argued that, in the early stages of the internal market, purchasers were more concerned with maintaining continuity with what had gone before and satisfying the wishes of GPs in the placement of contracts than with taking notice of the wishes of patients or their theoretical representatives. Given the NHS Executive goals of 'smooth take off' and 'steady-state' in the first year, at least, this is not surprising. Nonetheless, it suggests that trusts did not facilitate increased patient choice.

Second, the comparative lack of freedom to establish new services because of the strict rules about capital development, exacerbated by the introduction of the private finance initiative (PFI), made it difficult for trusts to create alternatives to established services, thus limiting increases in patient choice through this means. This point has been made by a number of commentators (Propper, 1995b; Caines, 1994; Centre for the Evaluation of Public Policy and Practice, 1997).

The bureaucracy introduced by the requirement placed on trusts to produce a 'business case' for all innovations may have limited their freedom to offer increased choice to patients. However, one can argue that its real purposes were to restrict the power of clinicians and ensure that developments were in line with national priorities. The use of a carefully defined process in which any proposed development had to demonstrate that it supported national priorities reduced clinicians' power to influence the future development of health services in the locality. A positive view of this was that it prevented what was termed 'decibel planning' where clinicians with strong power bases inside hospitals and good contacts in regional health authorities were able to secure funding for their 'pet' projects regardless of whether or not they should have been a priority. A negative view sees this process as taking the decision for the future planning of health care away from clinicians who were knowledgeable and placing it in the hands of managers who were less so. They were also more likely to ensure that developments were in line with national priorities. This strengthened the control of the political centre, but did little to increase patient choice.

This finding of the limited freedom eventually granted to trusts and the increased control of central government, conflicts with the impression of increased freedom to make decisions more quickly. This has been noted in a survey reported by Traynor (1995). However, as Harrison (1996) suggests, although trust managers have had greater freedom to implement certain internal managerial systems as they have seen fit, there have been a number of external pressures limiting freedom. The direction of service delivery was driven by centrally imposed directives, such as the Health of the Nation initiative, thereby limiting the freedom of trusts to determine local priorities.

At the heart of the difficulty in understanding why trusts have had so little freedom lies the following paradox: decentralisation of bureaucracy has been used as a means to make the NHS respond more effectively to central directives. An impartial observer of the structure of the NHS in 1998, knowing nothing of the aims of the reforms as expressed in *Working for Patients* might well conclude that the system created by the reforms was dominated by close control of individual hospitals by central government; notably through the use of central directives such as the Patient's Charter, Health of the Nation and waiting list initiatives. Official measures of the achievements of trusts have been made against the targets contained in these directives. The creation of trusts so that their managers were directly accountable to the Secretary of State has meant that the management agenda has been heavily influenced by central initiatives and that local influences on the management of the trust have been removed. This is exemplified by the abolition of regional health authorities, whose considerable power and budgetary control under the old system meant that they would have had the capacity to act as a 'filter' between the Department of Health/NHS Executive and individual trusts. From this one could argue that the effect of trusts, if not their rationale, has not been to create an internal market in health care, but to alter managerial procedures so that hospital management responds more directly to a national policy agenda.

Accountability

Working for Patients envisaged that trust status would increase the local population's sense of ownership and pride in their hospital. Critics of the reforms argued that the governance of trusts by boards appointed by, and reporting to, the Secretary of State reduced accountability to the local population. For example, the Association of Community Health Councils of England and Wales (1989) was sceptical about the new arrangements. However, as their solution was to ensure the representation of CHCs on trust boards one might argue that their concern about this issue was prompted by self-interest. A further, and more subtle, concern about the accountability of trusts was made by Ham (1991b), who argued that trusts were symbolic of an increased blurring between public and private sectors. He saw the introduction of trusts as likely to lead to more interdependence between the private and public sectors. NHS trusts as providers would have an incentive to sell services to private purchasers. He also expected joint ventures between trusts and the private sector to take place and argued that trusts would increasingly operate like private, not-for-profit hospitals.

Concerns about the accountability of trusts, particularly in relation to the composition of trust boards, have been frequently expressed. While in opposition, the Labour Party sought to make political capital from this issue (Labour Party, 1992). Labour claimed that non-executive directors with a business background had been disproportionately represented on trust boards – the implication being that their private sector background would make them more inclined to worry about the financial position of the trust rather than ensuring equity of access to and high clinical quality of the trust's services. It was also argued that business people would not understand or represent patients' wishes. It is unclear if these accusations are true. Ashburner (1994) presents similar figures for the number of trust non-executive directors with a business background, but reveals that over half of the non-executives surveyed had had recent involvement in voluntary groups such as charities or had been on Community Health Councils. Perhaps more worrying was a significant under-representation of people from minority ethnic groups and the 10% of non-executives who confessed to believing that commitment to the NHS was not an important attribute for holding their position.

A further criticism was that NHS trust boards were part of the 'quangocracy', disproportionately representing middle-class Conservative Party supporters (Labour Party, 1992). The Department of Health (1996b) produced their *Public Appointments Annual Report* partly in response to these concerns but only a tiny minority (those appointed to boards after July 1995) had to declare their political interests. So the suspicion that political appointments were made to smooth the passage of the 1991 reforms cannot be confirmed by these data (Harrison and New, 1997). However, since the 1997 election, 80% of trust appointees who did declare their political affiliations have been active on behalf of the Labour Party (Department of Health Press Release, 98/070).

Summary and conclusions

The evidence about NHS trusts can be summarised as follows.

- The quality and quantity of evidence on trusts is relatively low compared with, say, fundholding.

- There is only limited evidence that trust status made hospitals more efficient than they would otherwise have been.

- Although the conditions for competition between individual trusts existed in most parts of the country, there is no evidence of widespread competition between trusts. The incentives faced by purchasers and providers seem to have led to a series of bilateral monopolies.

- There is no evidence of trusts engaging in cream-skimming.

- It is difficult to prove that trust status was directly responsible for improvements in the quality of services. There are some concerns that different trusts had conflicting incentives which threatened the continuity of care.

- There is no evidence that trusts increased patient choice and there are several convincing arguments why it was impossible for them to do so.

- There is no evidence that trusts became more accountable to their local populations and there are anecdotal indications that trust boards were chosen, in part, for their political allegiances.

If the main aim of the quasi-market reform in the NHS was to provide market participants with greater incentives to improve efficiency and responsiveness to patients' needs, the evidence presented here appears to show little progress towards the latter and only lukewarm signs of the former. However, the experiences of trusts have not been uniform. In their study of the impact of competition on NHS trusts, Propper and Bartlett (1997) concluded that market forces had 'real though variable effects'. They found that where clinicians had more influence over decision-making, goals such as improving quality and throughput were likely to be given more weight than meeting financial targets. With respect to management costs, the newly created trusts did seem to have achieved lower costs than DMUs but this may have been because they were a self-selected group. It is clear that the reforms were accompanied by a high degree of regulation which limited trusts' freedoms and reduced the scope for competition between them. Rather, a set of bilateral monopolies developed between trusts and their larger HA purchasers (Propper, 1995a). In addition, as discussed elsewhere in this book, NHS purchasers were less effective than predicted at putting trusts under pressure to assess the strengths and weaknesses of their services in comparison with others. As a result, it is impossible to tell from the UK experience whether the impact of competition would have been detrimental or beneficial.

Part III: **Conclusion**

8 The reforms: success or failure or neither?

Julian Le Grand, Nicholas Mays and Jennifer Dixon

On balance, does the evidence, such as it is, indicate whether the internal market was a success or a failure? Whichever it was, what lessons can be drawn from the experiment? And have the lessons been learnt? Is their influence apparent in the proposals for the internal market's successor, as laid out in the Labour Government's White Paper, *The New NHS* (Secretary of State for Health, 1997)? This chapter addresses these questions.

However, before attempting to answer each of the questions, we reflect briefly on the inherent limitations of any effort to assess changes at the level of an entire health system and some of the particular difficulties faced in this instance.

The difficulties of researching health system change

The aim of this book has been to provide the research evidence to assess the impact of the quasi-market changes introduced in the NHS in 1991. From the outset, we were aware that this was an ambitious undertaking and that we were certain to fall short of our goals. In the field of complex organisational change, research can illuminate – but it can rarely deliver unequivocal answers to simple questions, such as whether innovation A is better than past practice B. The role of context guarantees that the answer has, at the very least, to specify the conditions and the nature of the participants necessary for the superiority of A over B. Nonetheless, we believe that it is useful, particularly for future historians, to have a record, however flawed, of all, or as many as possible, of the studies undertaken in the period after the changes, accompanied by some near-contemporary guidance on their interpretation.

The first difficulty encountered, seen throughout this book, was the lack of any comprehensive programme of evaluation covering the main dimensions of the quasi-market changes and their effects. There was no official support for independent evaluation in the early stages of the changes and resistance within the NHS to external research during the crucial period before the changes were implemented. As time has passed, an increasing body of research evidence has accumulated, but there are major gaps and limitations in it. For instance, the comparative absence of research on HAs as purchasers versus the attention given to the fundholding scheme. The advent of the quasi-market also disrupted and altered routine NHS data systems, further hampering simple monitoring.

The second main difficulty faced in producing a balance sheet of evidence concerned the changes themselves. The Conservative Government's own aims and predictions were typically abstract and expressed in general terms. However, more importantly, the changes were themselves multi-faceted and evolutionary. The proposals in *Working for Patients* (Secretaries of State for Health, 1989) were sketches with the details to be completed later during the process of implementation. As a result, policy makers and managers adapted the outlines which they had been presented with and muddled through. It can be argued that continuous adaptation and policy muddling is the strategy of choice in dynamic, democratic societies, particularly when dealing with large, multi-level institutions (Lindblom, 1979). The orthodoxy tends towards the exclusion of monolithic solutions to institutional design, relying instead on a range of strategies in specified contexts.

However, Klein (1995b) identifies the intellectual and political tensions inherent in the NHS changes themselves as contributing additionally to their emergent character. He argues that, 'a market system was injected into the shell of a hierarchic paternalistic institution, in which the providers .... had been able to exercise veto power over change ...' while at the same time the NHS remained centrally funded, centrally directed and centrally accountable. As a result, the reformed NHS failed to reach a steady state. It was constantly changing precisely because it was a hybrid with in-built tensions. This thesis helps explain the flexibility and elusiveness of many parts of the changes as they were implemented; for example, the varying interpretations placed on the concepts of a 'market' and of 'competition' within the NHS.

Another aspect of the changes themselves which affected the ability of researchers to capture what was going on related to the speed of some of the changes; particularly to the pace at which acute hospitals and others volunteered to become new NHS trusts. Comparative research between trusts and directly managed units (DMUs) rapidly became impossible. A related difficulty concerned the volunteer nature of parts of the reforms, especially early applications for trust status and fundholding. As a consequence, it was always hazardous to attempt to separate out the effects of trust or fundholding status from the selected nature of the participants and the attention devoted to them as pioneers.

The third difficulty encountered in trying to summarise the overall effects of the quasi-market was the potentially confounding effects of other factors. These included initiatives that were either already in place before 1991, but not necessarily related (e.g. the introduction of general management in the mid-1980s), or that were developed alongside such as the Patient's Charter. There were also major developments such as the private finance initiative (PFI) (Gaffney and Pollock, 1997) and a shift in responsibility for long-term care away from the NHS (House of Commons Health Committee, 1995b) which have been, it is argued, at least as significant as the direct effects of the quasi-market in changing the nature of health care in the UK. Again, these were not intrinsically related to the introduction of the quasi-market, but they may have obscured the effects of changes which were related to the use of market-type incentives. Perhaps the most potent complicating factor was the level of resources put into the NHS by the Government over time. Thus, substantially more money was invested in the period immediately after 1991 to smooth the implementation of the internal market. Rightly or wrongly, this book tries to concentrate on the main components of the internal market changes introduced in 1991/92 while recognising that this results in some over-simplification of the picture of change between then and early 1998.

The final difficulty of trying to focus on empirical research of the effects of the internal market changes was in relation to measurement. Many of the potential changes brought about by introducing quasi-market arrangements concern aspects of the health system such as culture, working practices and assumptions, knowledge, and the distribution of power and influence. The research methods of conventional health services are good at dealing with phenomena which are relatively straightforward to measure and to count. It is possible that the focus of studies and/or the tools which were used to track change simply failed to register important phenomena. Other subtle effects are hard to interpret. For example, it is likely that the development of the purchasing function encouraged managers, public health physicians and fundholders to become more aware of issues of health care quality, of cost and of the need to set priorities between different forms of care. This can be seen as a welcome development in a cash-limited system, but it is far more difficult to trace its effects through to measurable change in the pattern and volume of services delivered and their cost-effectiveness.

With these caveats in mind, we can answer the questions posed at the beginning of this chapter.

Success or failure

We begin by examining the record of whether the internal market was a success or a failure with respect to our criteria of *efficiency*, *equity*, *choice and responsiveness* and *accountability*.

Efficiency

With respect to overall efficiency, as shown in Chapter 3, Table 3.1, over the period since the reforms were introduced there was an increase in activity, as measured by the Cost-Weighted Activity Index (CWAI), that was greater than the increase in resources over that period. The cost per unit of activity went down and, hence, if the CWAI is accepted as a reasonable measure of NHS output (and, as discussed in previous chapters, there may be many reasons for *not* doing so), efficiency increased. The same was true of the period before the reforms; however, the increase was greater after 1991, suggesting that the rate of improvement in NHS efficiency increased.

This apparent improvement in efficiency in a crude sense happened despite well-publicised increases in transactions costs and specifically in management costs. These increases certainly occurred, although their origins and magnitude is a question of dispute. Although it is likely that a health care system based on contracts will be more expensive to organise than one based on integration of purchasers and providers, particularly when there are a large number of small purchasers alongside HAs in the form of fundholding general practices, the observed increase in NHS management costs has more complex origins. From official figures, the proportion of revenue attributable to administration in HAs and trusts reached about 12% in 1994/95, having been about 9% in 1988/89 (Audit Commission 1995a; Gerald Malone, Parliamentary Answer, 23 February 1995). However, the increases began before the implementation of the reforms and can just as convincingly be attributed to other changes in the NHS making new demands on managers, such as new requirements for improved corporate governance, and better complaints procedures. During 1995, for instance, 145 Executive Letters were issued by the centre – 43 more than in the previous year – in addition to 200 other management letters and instructions of various kinds (Harrison, 1997a). It is often forgotten that the period of the internal market reforms was also marked by increased central controls and upward accountability in the NHS which came at a price in management terms.

Moreover, because management costs are included in the overall measure of the costs of resources going into the NHS, and because activity increased faster than resources overall, any cost-inflationary impact that they had was more than outweighed by other positive factors contributing to greater efficiencies. Precisely what those positive factors were is difficult to determine from the evidence. With respect to hospital trusts, the main agents delivering the services captured in the CWAI, newly created trusts do seem to have had lower costs than non-trusts. Whether this was due to the reforms or due to their being a self-selected group remains controversial. Hospitals which opted for trust status in the early stages of the reforms may have either done so because they had lower unit costs or because they had reasonable expectations of being able to increase productivity for quite different reasons than the supposed greater freedom granted by trust status. There is also conflicting evidence as to whether trusts adopted more efficient techniques, and, if they did, whether this was attributable to the reforms or to other factors such as the general march of medical technology. It is interesting to note that the degree of competition between hospital trusts did not seem to be significantly associated with higher productivity. Overall, the conflicting nature of the evidence on trusts and the impact of trust status can be attributed simply to the very small numbers of studies on any aspect of their behaviour and the short time available for comparisons.

Because purchasing as a role did not exist before the reforms, it is impossible to judge whether it has been performed more efficiently after 1991. In addition, it must be remembered that HAs and fundholders (perhaps the most interesting contemporary comparison) were charged with different responsibilities and so were not strictly comparable. However, there is some evidence concerning the relative efficiency of different kinds of purchasers derived from comparisons of general practices served by the two approaches. For example, there was an initial difference in the rate of growth of prescribing costs between fundholders and non-fundholders; and the difference in levels persisted, although the differentials stopped growing. Fundholders also generated more 'savings' or surpluses than HAs. On the other hand, of all the purchasing models surveyed, fundholding appeared to have the highest transactions costs. This may be because fundholders were more effective in their contracting; or it may be because smaller units have proportionately larger transactions costs – although among the studies of fundholding we surveyed, there was no direct evidence of either economies or diseconomies of scale in management and administrative costs. (More collective forms of GP budget-holding such as total purchasing might be expected to be less costly per capita to manage than single-practice fundholding, but here too there is little evidence of any economies of scale, perhaps due to these being offset by the additional coordination costs of managing a budget collectively across increasing numbers of independent practices). The higher transactions costs may lead to relative technical inefficiency; and this may partly or wholly offset any gains in allocative efficiency that result from any improvements in quality, choice and responsiveness that the smaller purchasing units are able to achieve. Indeed, it has been argued that not only did fundholding increase administrative costs for trusts, but it encouraged the negotiation of marginal cost deals (see below). In both cases, it is argued, the process was subsidised by the HAs which, for example, bore the additional costs of fundholders' lower prices. As a result HAs faced higher prices and were, therefore, more likely to run deficits quite apart from any pressures they faced from rising emergency admissions. Seen in this light, not only were fundholders and HAs not strictly comparable as purchasers, they were operating in two separate markets with different rules.

Equity

The principal equity issue that worried many analysts at the start of the internal market was the danger of cream-skimming: the deliberate selection of patients both by hospitals and by fundholding practices who were easier or less costly to treat in order to protect budgets (Scheffler 1989; Le Grand and Bartlett, 1993). However, there is no evidence that this has been a problem, either on the purchaser or provider side although it is not easy to study. Given that several parts of the internal market apparently offered incentives for cream-skimming, it is not immediately obvious why this particular dog did not bark. One explanation might be that the professional ethic of medical practitioners restrained them from denying treatment to those most obviously in need. Another is that the incentives to cream-skim were actually quite limited. In the case of GP fundholders, for instance, perhaps the most obvious candidates for engaging in this practice, there was an 'insurance' scheme by which fundholders were not liable for the extra costs associated with very expensive patients – a fact which significantly reduced any incentive they may have had to exclude such patients from their lists. In addition, unlike the situation in the USA with respect to health maintenance organisations which bear some similarities with fundholders, a fundholding GP's personal financial well-being was not directly dependent on the health of the fundholding budget, thus sharply reducing the incentives for cream-skimming. This feature of fundholding reflects the wider reality that, throughout the reform period, the NHS continued to be managed and regarded explicitly as a public service rather than a system in which providers or purchasers could put their financial targets ahead of 'needed' health care.

Instead, the chief equity concern that exercised press, public and politicians was the so-called 'two-tier' issue, whereby the patients of GP fundholders apparently received preferential treatment over patients being paid for by HAs. That this did indeed occur is borne out by most studies of the question. The only area where there remains significant disagreement concerns the extent to which this arose because fundholders were better purchasers or because they were better resourced. Whether or not fundholders were systematically 'over-funded' in certain regions, as more practices joined the scheme, it became apparent that fundholding practices were increasingly being shifted towards fairer capitation funding.

However, it is worth noting two points with respect to two-tierism. First, no-one has claimed that it resulted in patients of non-fundholding practices being actually worse off than before the reforms. If they were not, then the problem was one of differential rates of improvement, rather than an absolute worsening for one group. Second, the phenomenon arose not because of the intrinsic nature of an internal market, but because this particular internal market had two different kinds of purchaser. Two-tierism was not a product of the internal market as a concept, but simply of the way that this particular one was set up. Fundamentally, as West (1997) points out, there remains an inescapable degree of inequity in giving GPs budgets and incentives to use them, because if they are able to negotiate lower prices for the same volume of services, their patients will have an advantage over other practices' populations. Two kinds of purchasers will inevitably lead to two-tierism, if one kind of purchaser is more successful at its job than the other.

Quality

Our review of the evidence with respect to the principal providers of secondary care, hospital trusts, found no evidence of improved quality that could be attributed to trust status. However, the reviews of the evidence with respect to purchasing did find some improvements, mostly attributable to fundholding. There was a greater provision of outreach services by fundholders than non-fundholders; and they obtained quicker admission for their patients and, more generally, more response from providers. GP and locality commissioning schemes also had some successes in achieving greater responsiveness from providers, although the most successful looked the most like fundholders in that they had some form of budget and clear responsibility for commissioning certain services which was independent of the HA (Glennerster et al., 1996). The Berkshire Integrated Purchasing Project – a pioneer TPP – seemed to be producing greater satisfaction among its patients compared to a control group of similar neighbouring practices (Walsh et al., 1997).

It is possible to obtain some more general indication of satisfaction from the annual survey of the public's attitudes to the NHS carried out by the British Social Attitudes Survey. Since 1983, this has asked questions on the level of satisfaction with the running of the NHS in general, on the level of satisfaction with specific services and on attitudes towards increased public spending on the NHS. Dissatisfaction with the overall running of the NHS rose substantially during the 1980s, before the reforms, from 25% in 1983 to 47% in 1990 – the year before *Working for Patients* was implemented. In the 1990s, dissatisfaction fell, reaching a low of 38% in 1993. However, findings from the most recent survey carried out in 1996 indicated that the upward trend in dissatisfaction had resumed. Dissatisfaction with the overall running of the NHS had risen to 50%, its highest level ever (Judge *et al.*, 1997).

There are obvious difficulties in interpreting levels of satisfaction and dissatisfaction with the NHS and the trends are open to a number of interpretations. For example, it is hard to determine the extent to which the trends reflect changes in the NHS itself or shifts towards a more consumerist, demanding culture outside the NHS. If the former, were the key factors the internal market, the Patient's Charter, an overall scarcity of resources – or something more ephemeral such as a media-orchestrated 'crisis in the NHS'? Increasing dissatisfaction could well reflect rising, but as yet unfulfilled, expectations as to the appropriate quality of service which the NHS should deliver.

The dip in dissatisfaction in the early 1990s could have indicated that the NHS reforms were beginning to be seen to work. However, a more compelling explanation for the rise in satisfaction in the period immediately after the introduction of the internal market was the unusually large injection of new money. This happened for three years in succession from 1990 and helped allay fears that the Service was underfunded. Backing for this interpretation comes from Mulligan and Judge (1997) who have shown that trends in dissatisfaction with the NHS as a whole have closely matched public perceptions as to whether the NHS was underfunded or not. The increased levels of funding in the early 1990s thus enabled the reforms, together with other high profile initiatives such as the Waiting List Initiative and the Patient's Charter, to get the best possible start. More recently, however, the NHS has faced much more constrained levels of funding resulting in an almost daily diet of media 'doom and gloom' stories. It is not difficult to see how the poorer funding position, combined with an awareness of deficiencies in performance highlighted by the Patient's Charter and newer initiatives such as the publication of hospital league tables, should have led to an increase in dissatisfaction with the general running of the NHS.

Another potential, but very different, indicator of quality is that of waiting lists. These were subject to a series of initiatives both before and after the adoption of an internal market. Waiting lists have continued to grow in the 1990s as they did in the 1980s. The number of people waiting for ordinary (inpatient) and day treatment combined rose from 948,200 in March 1991 to 1,071,100 in September 1994. It fell back slightly to 1,061,600 in September 1996 and increased to 1,164,400 in March 1997 (Le Grand and Vizard, 1998). By September 1997, the number had risen still further to 1,207,500. Provisional figures released in February 1998 showed that 1,262,300 patients were waiting in December 1997, an increase of 54,700 (4.5%) over the previous quarter and 14.2% over the same quarter a year earlier.

However, although waiting lists have been growing in length, mean waiting times have been falling. The Conservative Government was successful in eliminating the small group of people waiting for very long periods of time for treatment. And people waiting for NHS treatment have, on average, been waiting for shorter periods of time. Thus in September 1991, of the total number of people waiting for inpatient and day treatment, 11.8% (111,840 people) had been waiting for between one year and two years, and 4.6% (43,598 people) had been waiting for more than two years. The proportion of people waiting for between one and two years steadily declined to 5.8% (62,124 people) in September 1994, and to 1.4% (14,862 people) in September 1996. However, the figures point to a reversal of this trend in late 1996 and 1997. In September 1996, according to official figures, 1.4% (15,000 people) were waiting for between 12 and 17 months. This proportion increased sharply to 2.7% (31,160 people) in March 1997 and to 4.7% (56,900) in September 1997.

Waiting times of more than two years were totally eliminated in March 1993, and had not reappeared by September 1996. The current Patient's Charter standard aims for the treatment of all patients within 18 months of being placed on the waiting list. In September 1996, there were only 25 patients recorded as having waited more than 18 months in England, which is less than 0.1%. By the end of September the following year, this number had risen to 818 or 0.8% of the waiting list. The latest provisional figures from the Department of Health indicate that, by the end of December 1997, this number had risen to 974, but remained no more than 0.8% of the total list. Although there was a reduction in average waiting time in the mid-1990s and, particularly, in longer waits, the average waiting time in the 1990s as a whole was broadly the same as it was in the 1960s and 1970s (Hamblin *et al.*, 1998).

These data taken together suggest that the NHS is continuing to maintain a standard of elective service based on an average wait of around 13 to 14 weeks, but it is impossible to tell whether the internal market has significantly contributed to or hindered this. What is plain is that maintaining the 13–14 week average wait overall requires record increases in, and record levels of, elective activity. For example, despite an increase of over 800,000 in the annual rate of treatment of patients on the waiting list between 1990/91 and 1994/95, the waiting list lengthened by over 100,000, as over a million more patients were referred to it. It appears that, at least as far as average waiting times are concerned, the NHS has to run faster and faster to stay in the same place.

Choice and responsiveness

The evidence suggests that choice for patients has not increased. One study found no increase in choice of hospital for elderly patients as a result of the development of purchaser–provider negotiations. A study by Fotaki (1998) of the impact of the reforms on choices offered to patients for cataract surgery found no increase in choice of either procedure or provider for patients of both fundholders and non-fundholders; indeed, if anything, choice for both purchasers and patients seemed to have been reduced. However, there was a limited increase in the amount of information given to patients.

With respect to HAs and responsiveness, there is anecdotal evidence of user consultations and forums, but no systematic information on the type, extent and consequences of such activities for patients. Incentives for HAs to respond to individual patient preferences seemed to be weak (compared with, for example, those to respond to NHS Executive directives to achieve centrally determined targets). No 'exit' was possible by dissatisfied users, and methods of expressing patient 'voice' (e.g. through Community Health Councils, or HA non-executive directors) were limited and little altered, if at all, by the reforms. On the other hand, HAs were encouraged to undertake more assessment of population needs which, when linked to contracting might, in theory, affect what services were provided for patients by clinicians. However, any effects of this were indirect and not easily detectable.

Fundholders appeared more successful than other forms of purchaser in obtaining responsiveness from providers. However, there was little evidence of increased choice for their patients. GP and locality commissioners were motivated to obtain views of patients, but there is relatively little evidence concerning the impact of their efforts on services. Total purchasers appeared to be more reluctant to consult patients directly, but appeared to offer more choice to patients than a control group of non-total purchasers in one project site. Like fundholders, GPs involved in TPPs had been encouraged, by the way in which the scheme was presented, to regard themselves as well-informed agents for their patients who, therefore, did not need systematically to canvass patients' views. They were also aware, in many cases, of the difficulties inherent in efforts to secure patient involvement, which HAs have faced to a similar degree.

There is no evidence that trusts have increased patient choice and several convincing arguments why it has been impossible for them to do so. West (1997) argues from his extensive experience as a management consultant and analyst in the post-reform NHS that the reform process has not really penetrated to the 'factory floor' (i.e. to the working of individual clinics and clinician–patient relations); most staff still 'treat patients as a guaranteed commodity which will never go away'.

Accountability

There is a general view that 'upward' accountability of HAs to the centre is high, and that for GP fundholders relatively low. GP and locality commissioners were ostensibly more accountable than fundholders to HAs, but clashes occurred in practice. For total purchasers, there has been little emphasis on accountability considerations other than ensuring conventional financial accountability. Although trusts were clearly accountable to purchasers, there is no evidence that trusts have become more accountable to their local populations and there is some suggestion that trust boards were chosen in part for their political allegiances. There is no sense in which the decision-making of either HAs or trusts has become more transparent to the public.

Overall: little change?

Perhaps the most striking conclusion to arise from this survey of the evidence is how little overall measurable change there seems to have been related to the core structures and mechanisms of the internal market. Indeed, in some areas where significant changes might have been expected, there were none. For instance, there seems to have been no difference between fundholders and non-fundholders in referral rates for elective surgery, despite the fact that one set of GPs was making referrals from a fixed budget for which they were responsible and the other set were not. There were signs that individual TPPs which set out to alter the level of use of acute hospital services by developing alternatives could bring about appreciable changes. However, in general it is hard not to agree with a leader from *The Independent* (25 February 1997) which concluded that, 'The Thatcher-Clarke reforms – GP fundholding, the quasi-market – are neither pernicious nor notably efficacious.' West's recently published personal review of the same terrain comes to a strikingly similar conclusion: 'There is no reason to believe that the NHS has got manifestly worse under the reforms' (West, 1997). Although this may be seen as a paltry result given all the effort and resources which have been devoted to a huge organisational change since 1991, it is also reassuring, given the very real potential for destabilising the system inherent in the radicalism of the original reform proposals.

This apparent absence of obvious change attributable to the internal market may be because there was indeed little change. Or it may be because there *was* change, but the studies concerned either focused on the wrong indicators or focused on the right indicators, but their deficiencies of technique were such that they could not pick up the relevant changes in those indicators.

It is clear that in some, possibly unmeasurable ways, the NHS *has* changed fundamentally since the 1991 internal market reforms. Purchasing has involved significant organisational change. The criteria we have used to evaluate the evidence have not related directly to measuring this type of cultural and managerial shift. Our sense is that there has been a considerable degree of cultural change involving HAs, fundholding and non-fundholding practices. This is especially in terms of the extra attention being paid to the concerns of GPs of all types and an alteration in GPs' standing within the system, if not always in their coercive power. Smith and colleagues (Smith *et al.*, 1997b; Smith and Shapiro, 1997) have shown the numerous ways in which new partnerships are developing between groups of practices and with HAs; and it would now be unthinkable not to involve GPs and, increasingly, other primary care professionals in local commissioning processes in one way or another. Also, there seems to have been a considerable increase in cost-consciousness throughout the Service. Finally, there appears to be a wide, but not total, agreement that the device of separately identifying the purchaser role from that of the provider has proved broadly successful and should remain in some form. At the very least, the contracting process has probably forced some greater clarity into the interchange between purchasers and providers as to what should be provided, for whom, to what standard and at what price.

But why did these organisational and cultural changes not result in more demonstrable impacts in the areas that we have investigated? Although it is possible that there were significant changes, and the studies that we have surveyed simply did not pick them up, this seems unlikely to be the whole explanation. Although no one can be more aware than the authors of this book of the problems with the published evidence, there do seem to have been a sufficient number of competent studies that would have picked up changes and differences if they had been large enough.

The explanation must, therefore, lie with the way in which the internal market was implemented. And here there is a ready economic answer: *the incentives were too weak and the constraints were too strong.* Put another way, the motivations for change were relatively weak, especially when compared with the pressures for stability from outside. For markets of any kind (pure, internal or quasi) to work, all the relevant agents must be motivated by the relevant market signals; and they must have freedom of action to respond to those motivations (Le Grand and Bartlett, 1993). Yet most of the key actors in the NHS internal market had, for a variety of reasons, little direct incentive to move in the direction indicated by market developments; and both the actors and the market signals themselves were heavily constrained by central government intervention. So, HAs could not keep or invest any surplus they generated, leaving them with the sole incentive to come in exactly on budget. The investment and, even more significantly, the pricing policies of trusts were strictly controlled; as a consequence, the opportunities for competition between them were highly restricted. HAs could not switch providers easily without destabilising them; also they were instructed to bail out trusts in financial difficulties, with the consequence that for many trusts budget constraints became viewed as 'soft', rather than 'hard'. Again, this had implications for competition. Trusts not only had limited opportunities to compete with one another; they had little incentive to do so, knowing that they could not keep any surpluses if they succeeded and that they would be bailed out if they failed. More generally, both HAs and trusts were not really treated as independent agents, but viewed more as partially decentralised instruments of central government policy. They were certainly not in any sense, free market agents.

All this is reinforced by the evidence concerning the relative performance of HAs and the one agent not mentioned above: GP fundholders. HAs had little incentive to develop a surplus on their budgets, because it would simply disappear at the year's end. At the same time, they were subject to a stream of directives from the centre – concerning priorities, waiting lists, *Health of the Nation* targets, etc. They were also under considerable pressure, both from the centre and from local interests, not to destabilise local providers by any abrupt changes in their purchasing strategies. It is, therefore, hardly surprising that many of them concentrated on simply keeping the system going while trying to meet central priorities. In contrast, fundholders could retain their surpluses and use them to improve their facilities. In this connection, it is of interest to note that if incentives were reduced, for example, when savings in drug budgets led to reduced allocations in the following year, their behaviour changed significantly; they were less likely to strive to find less expensive drugs for their patients. But fundholders also had strong non-pecuniary incentives – arising both from their professional ethos and from direct patient pressure – to see that their patients were promptly and effectively treated. Equally significantly, they were less constrained than HAs; they were subject to a weak accountability regime and, being relatively small, could switch their purchasing without massively destabilising providers. Instead, they represented an attractive source of marginal income to trusts. They had both more opportunity and more capacity to be innovative. It is no coincidence that the area where it has been easiest to detect some significant changes is where the incentives were strongest and the constraints the weakest.

Other operational difficulties with the internal market concerned its capacity, and the difficulties of promoting entry and exit. Most markets operate with some spare capacity so that businesses can, if the circumstances permit, expand to take work from their competitors. However, the NHS had spent the previous 40 years attempting to plan to make the fullest use of its hospitals and other facilities to avoid waste (Dawson, 1995). So capacity was at a premium. Furthermore, entry into this quasi-market was and remains extremely difficult because of the scale and complexity of investment required to set up a modern acute hospital; while for a hospital or other provider to 'exit' from the market through closure often encountered insuperable political difficulties. As a result, although there have been isolated instances of trusts' activities driving other trusts out of business, the predominant response to competition in the internal market, paradoxically, has been trust mergers within some wider strategic framework based on the view that services are interdependent.

Another way of characterising the limitations of the reforms from a market point of view is to point to the inherent contradictions in the notion of a 'managed market' in which policy makers and managers have sought to reconcile the objectives of competitive efficiency with other NHS strategic goals such as equity of access (Flynn and Williams, 1997; Spurgeon et al., 1997). Long before the change of Government in May 1997, we find the Department of Health encouraging the Service to find the appropriate balance between competition and 'constructive cooperation' while also acknowledging the pragmatic advantages of *contestability* – the *possibility* that alternative providers might displace the existing ones in the absence of current competition (Department of Health, 1994).

Finally, a yet more fundamental explanation for the failure of the internal market to have the impact its proponents hoped may lie in the motivations of the actors concerned. For markets to work effectively, individuals need to be motivated by the furtherance of their own interests. However, those working in the Service often continued to see themselves as engaged in the provision of public services based on relations of mutual trust (Broadbent and Laughlin, 1997; Flynn et al., 1996). In part, contracting had less impact than was expected because of the difficulty of specifying the content of services with sufficient clarity for contracting without threatening the relations of trust, professional discretion and long term cooperation on which the effective production of many services largely depended (Flynn *et al.*, 1996). Checkland (1997) showed that the form of the contracts was not an important element in the way in which the contracting process was translated into the production of services. Relationships between purchasers and providers continued to develop alongside the formal contracting process as much as through it, according to Spurgeon *et al.* (1997). All in all, both purchasers and providers were not perhaps as single-minded in the pursuit of a narrowly defined self-interest as the internal market required; in the terminology of one of the authors, they continued to operate more like 'knights' than like 'knaves' (Le Grand, 1997).

The lessons to be learned

Even though much of the evidence is inconclusive, there are some lessons to be learned from the British internal market experience. First, although we do not have direct evidence, because assessing the overall effect of the internal market in a definitive way is almost certainly impractical, most analysts of the internal market would agree on the following: the split between purchaser and provider, together with the development of contracts or service agreements between purchasers and providers that the market necessitated, were desirable innovations which should be retained in any future development of the system – despite the fact that, for some commentators, the extent of regulation excessively weakened the incentives inherent in the system. However, there would be less agreement on the desirability of the other key aspect of the internal market – the introduction of competition – and this is discussed below.

On the purchasing side, if the policy aims are to promote *quality*, *choice* and *responsiveness*, then it seems to be important to have devolved purchasing with some degree of GP (or other local) involvement in, or even leadership of, the purchasing or commissioning process. Further, the evidence, whether from fundholding, locality commissioning or total purchasing, seems to suggest that the best way to sustain productive GP involvement is for the agency, of whatever kind, to have a measure of budgetary control. The budget gives a degree of potential leverage over providers that simple advice or exhortation does not; holding budgets across several practices, as in the TPPs, also plays a role in cementing these organisations together. Increasingly integrated budgets allow commissioners to shift resources productively between sectors, particularly between secondary and primary or community care.

The conclusions with respect to *equity* and *efficiency* are not so clear cut. Devolution of power to smaller purchasing and commissioning units, of whatever kind, inevitably means that some will do different things from others. This in turn, is likely to mean that the more effective purchasers may provide a better service overall and certainly better aspects of part of their service than others. This has obvious implications for both the equity and the efficiency of service delivery. However, if the effective strategies of the more successful purchasers are known to the centre in a national service, then these can be used to lever up the performance of the poor performers. The most important prerequisite for equity appears to be rather that each purchasing agent should have equal resources relative to the composition of its population. To insist that every local group do the same would stifle innovation as well as undermine the rationale for local purchasing of services. Recent advances in formula funding suggest that fundholding is possible on a subdistrict level.

There are other efficiency problems that appear to arise with devolved purchasing. Smaller units may have problems of managerial capacity and support; their risk pool may be too small, leading to budget fragility (although here the precise size of population is crucial because even purchasers of 30–40,000 patients appear to be able to manage the clinical risk of most rare and costly referrals (Bachmann and Bevan, 1996)); they may encounter difficulties in obtaining the necessary experience, expertise or personnel to carry out effective purchasing. For example, the Audit Commission's investigation into the purchasing of specialised services identified a scarcity of expertise in the NHS as a whole (Audit Commission, 1997). Also smaller purchasing units can create problems for provider planning and stability; the provision and maintenance of expensive facilities may require guarantees of future income streams that are difficult to obtain from a host of small purchasers.

This raises the general question of the appropriate size of purchasing unit, or, more generally, the appropriate level of decision-making for purchasing or commissioning. It is possible that different services are best purchased at different levels. It may be that neither fully centralised purchasing nor completely devolved purchasing is appropriate for all services. There are inevitable trade-offs between: minimising total management costs; the richness of specialist knowledge; having an appropriate pattern of purchasing sensitive to patients' needs; the level of financial risk; and ensuring good access to services (Smith *et al.*, 1997b).

Table 8.1: **Possible distribution of purchasing responsibilities for different types of services**

Type of service	Examples	Population size	Purchasing level
Rare	Organ transplantation Neurosciences	>500,000	Regional/central
Common and expensive	'Routine' emergency care	50,000–500,000	Health authority/PCGs
	Elective surgery	10,000–50,000	PCGs
Common and cheap	Community health services	3,000–10,000	GP practices

Table 8.1 illustrates how some of these trade-offs might be played out in terms of the appropriate level of purchasing. Expensive and/or rare, unpredictable services where financial risk needs to be spread over a large population (although this aspect is probably less important) and where expertise is unlikely to reside at practice level, might need to be purchased at regional or supra-district level (e.g. intensive care, organ transplantation, neurosciences, secure units, trauma care), perhaps with populations between 500,000 and 2 million people. There may even be services which should be planned nationally: forensic psychiatry might be an example. In turn, 'routine' emergency care such as general medicine and geriatrics might be purchased on behalf of populations of 50–500,000 by current HAs. Elective treatments and routine tests, and investigations such as those included in the fundholding scheme and other services such as palliative care, might be purchased by primary care-based organisations with 10–50,000 populations, leaving community health services to be purchased by organisations responsible for 3–10,000 people, say, individual general practices. Services such as

those for the seriously mentally ill and those with learning difficulties which require specialised purchasing expertise and effective links between health and local social services could be planned at district and local authority level; they would have joint budgets for specific services such as community psychiatric nursing delegated to, say, groups of general practices, to purchase specific packages of care for clients at a population level of 10–50,000.

There are some other lessons that arise from the literature with respect to purchasing and contracting. First, although budgetary control appears to be desirable for achieving changes in the desired direction, it is clearly not sufficient on its own. The Audit Commission noted, for instance, that many fundholders were failing to secure the expected benefits for patients (Audit Commission, 1996). It seemed that, although fundholding may have created greater potential for change, it was only the innovative and well-organised practices within fundholding that transformed patient care. As the report argued, most fundholders had had only modest ambitions, perhaps because they tailored those ambitions to what they felt they had control over. In consequence, most services in fundholding practices were delivered in the same way by the same providers with few measurable extra benefits to patients. Many of the successes of GP commissioning also appear to depend on innovative practices. It may, therefore, be that one test of different models of health service organisation is their ability to release the innovator and to sustain innovations once introduced.

Second, although there are areas of consensus, it is important to point out that the interpretation of whether the changes which occurred are good or bad varies. For example, there have been questions as to whether greater practice-based care is better care or a more efficient use of resources than care provided in other settings. In the case of 'two-tierism', this can be interpreted, on the one hand, as a catalyst to the levelling-up of the quality of health care and a necessary interim product of the 1991 NHS reforms. On the other hand, a 'two-tier' system can be seen as a major equity problem, benefiting the patients of affluent fundholders at the expense of smaller and less affluent practices with poorer populations in greater need of care.

On the provider side, the principal lesson concerns the question of competition. For the reasons already outlined, the competitive element within the internal market was not actually as great as its proponents had hoped, although still apparent in some areas and for some services (Propper and Bartlett, 1997). This may have been a major reason why the internal market did not have the dramatic consequences predicted. It appears that, if an internal market is to work properly, real competition must be encouraged. Providers must be allowed to succeed (and to retain the rewards of their success); they must be allowed to fail (and to suffer the consequences of their failure); they should have freedom of action in key areas of competitive practice, such as pricing. Overall, and most importantly if the argument at the end of the last section is correct, it is important to get both the incentives and the constraints right.

But all of this begs the fundamental question of whether there should be competition at all. Here our review of the evidence offers little help. Because, in practice, competition was patchy, we do not know, on balance, whether its impact was detrimental or beneficial – or what the consequences would have been if it had been extended. The issue of the relative merits of a non-competitive resource allocation system versus a competitive one is not one that can be resolved straightforwardly by the evidence reviewed. The evidence, such as it is, indicates the contradictory and ambiguous nature of both national policy and local behaviour in the internal market, with a constant tension between, on the one hand collaboration and cooperation and, on the other, competition and managerial surveillance of health professionals (Williams and Flynn, 1997). Thus Propper and Bartlett (1997) have shown that, whereas generally the way in which the internal market has been 'managed' has greatly reduced the theoretical incentives embedded within its structure and has reduced competition, this process has not been uniform and has had different consequences depending on whether managerial or clinical influence has predominated within trusts. They argue that where general managers have predominated, the pursuit of financial goals has assumed pre-eminence, but that where clinician control has been stronger (e.g. under a system of clinical directorates), other goals such as improving quality and increasing throughput have been more salient. They conclude:

Under some circumstances patient interests may be well served by the introduction of efficiency-improving competitive markets which undermine the 'vested interests' of the medical profession, while in other circumstances trusts may be able to exploit their monopoly power at the expense of consumers. The Department of Health's attempt to minimize the potentially adverse impact of the quasi-market on levels of health service provision, and to minimize some of the more inequitable effects of markets appear to have been only partially successful. However, attempts to regulate the market may be ineffective where trusts can effectively evade regulation, and probably give rise to perverse and unintended incentives.
(Propper and Bartlett, 1997)

The Labour White Paper: *The New NHS*

In December 1997, the Labour Government published a White Paper in England (Secretary of State for Health, 1997) proposing a further reorganisation of the Health Service. Do the new proposals suggest that the lessons of the internal market experience have been learned? Do they constitute, as the Government has claimed, a 'third way'?

The most relevant of the new proposals for this discussion are summarised below.

- The purchaser/provider split is to remain. But the emphasis is to be on cooperative relationships, not competitive or adversarial ones. Health improvement programmes, which are local health and health services strategies, have to be agreed with all relevant parties, including local authorities as well as purchasers, and trusts. As a last resort, purchasers can switch their purchasing away from their current providers.

- Purchasers are to become primary care groups (PCGs), led by GPs and community nurses. PCGs will include up to 50 GPs and cover around 100,000 population. PCGs will hold budgets; they will be able to retain surpluses, which can be spent on services or facilities of benefit to patients. All GPs will be required to join PCGs, but PCGs can begin to operate simply in an advisory capacity to the HA (Level 1), before graduating to the control of their own budgets and to merging their commissioning and primary care provider roles in new primary care trusts (Level 4). The current trusts will remain and will also be able to retain surpluses.

- Fundholders will be absorbed into PCGs. HAs will lose their purchasing role, except for certain highly specialised services, but will become the lead for Health Improvement Programmes and instrument for PCG accountability.

- Annual contracts will be replaced by three-year service agreements.

- A new performance 'framework', with new performance indicators emphasising effectiveness and outcomes, will be put in place.

- There will be two new national bodies: one to set standards – the National Institute for Clinical Excellence (NICE); the other to enforce them – the Commission for Health Improvement (CHIMP).

The first striking point about these proposals is that, despite some rhetoric to the contrary, key elements of the internal market are to be retained. The purchaser/provider split remains. The negotiated arrangements between purchasers and providers are unlikely to differ significantly from current contracts, except perhaps in being rather more long-term. The new GP-led commissioning organisations will hold budgets, and so will look remarkably like the existing total purchasing groups of fundholding practices (TPPs) – which some people regard as the ultimate extension of fundholding. Trusts and PCGs are both to be allowed to retain their surpluses. And purchasers will be able to switch to other providers if they are dissatisfied with their existing ones: so competition, or at least contestability (the potential *in extremis* for competition), will remain.

All this seems consistent with the lessons to be learned from the internal market experience which were laid out above. As noted, the purchaser/provider split was generally thought to be one of the more successful elements of the internal market. The evidence on the experience of different purchasing models showed that GPs with budgets tended to be the most effective purchasers. We noted the importance of retention of surpluses for purchasers and trusts. And it would be impossible to retain the purchaser/provider split without some possibility of competition. If purchasers did not hold the ultimate sanction of being able to take their business elsewhere, they would have no lever over providers. However, we also noted that contestability was likely to be limited, in practice, in most settings and that the nature of health care meant that longer-term collaborative relations between purchasers and providers were frequently as, or more, important for service development – thereby supporting the proposals to move to longer-term service level agreements rather than annual contracts.

There are areas where problems might arise. For instance, is 100,000 the 'right' size for the PCGs? What incentives are there for GPs to take part and what sanctions will PCG leaders have over 'free-riding' colleagues? GPs do not always find it easy to work together, particularly when they have not chosen their colleagues. The experience of the TPPs in their first live year of purchasing suggests that the smaller groups did better, largely because they had less need to invest in inter-practice organisational development (Mays et al., 1998a, 1998b). Time will tell whether the larger TPPs in some sense catch up with the smaller, less complex pilots. Another concern relates to the size of the PCGs. The bigger the commissioning authority, in a politically sensitive, highly managed system, the greater the danger that their purchasing constitutes too large a portion of local trusts' income, thereby restricting their ability to shift business elsewhere, if necessary. This problem was particularly acute for the old HAs, which, as we noted, often found that their attempts to alter their pattern of purchasing significantly were stymied by the threat of collapse (either genuine or synthetic) from the trusts losing business. On the other hand, as we also noted, there are some services which may be better purchased at the level of larger population groupings; and, if there is only to be one kind of principal purchaser, the proposed size may be the best compromise.

Another potential problem with PCGs relates to the cost of managing the 500 devolved purchasing organisations in England which will result from the setting up of PCGs, given the fact that the vast majority of the purchasing responsibility is currently exercised by around 90 HAs. Despite the fact that money will be saved by the abolition of single-practice fundholding and some HA functions can be taken over by PCGs, allowing a reallocation of management costs, there are doubts about whether the government is realistic in aiming to *reduce* overall management spending while initiating PCGs. The experience with the first-wave TPPs highlighted two factors: the scale of the organisational development task required to link previously independent practices; and the fact that those pilots which were best able to achieve their own purchasing/commissioning objectives, at least in the first year, tended to spend more on management than other pilots (Mays *et al.*, 1998a, 1998b) and, in any event more than the Government is likely to allow PCGs in future. Within the range of population sizes in the total purchasing scheme (approximately 12–85,000 patients), there did not appear to be obvious economies of scale in management costs (Posnett *et al.*, 1998). Management and transactions costs were one of the main weaknesses of the previous internal market and could remain a problem for the future.

There may also be problems concerning the 'replacement' of competition by cooperation. For cooperation to work, particularly between purchasers and providers, there have to be either no conflicts of interest (unlikely) or else mechanisms for resolving any conflicts which arise. It is possible that keeping the possibility of competition as a last resort is just such a mechanism; and, again, given the difficulties of ensuring a properly competitive environment, it may be that this is an appropriate compromise. However, the precise effects of the new shift of emphasis will depend on the detailed, day-to-day interpretation of the future guidance and regulations by managers throughout the NHS.

Perhaps the area of greatest worry concerns the role of the centre. The performance management framework in the Labour White Paper is quite centralist in tone with a large number of performance indicators (37 are currently proposed) and with the introduction of institutions (NICE and CHIMP) designed to monitor performance and, if necessary to intervene. There will also be a series of nationally determined service frameworks which will govern the limits of the discretion permitted to the PCGs as commissioners of services. Care will have to be taken that the Government does not make the mistakes of its predecessor in paying lip service to the ideal of decentralisation while at the same time trying to retain a strong grip from the centre

Overall, the White Paper's proposals deserve a guarded welcome, not least because they have preserved some of the features of the internal market that, as best as can be determined, have been demonstrated to work, while dispensing with some of its less successful aspects.

Unsurprisingly, problems remain. But here another aspect of the proposals is to be applauded: their avoidance of a 'big-bang' introduction of untested reforms. Instead there is the staged development of PCGs over five to ten years. The White Paper demonstrates an important lesson: that we *can* learn from experience.

Summary

- Post-reform, NHS activity rose faster than resources (and rose at a relatively faster rate than before the reforms). This suggests that, overall, despite some well-publicised increases in transactions costs, there was an increase in efficiency in the NHS that is attributable to the reforms.

- Although analysts widely predicted that cream-skimming would create equity problems, no cream-skimming was observed in practice. The principal equity concern arose from the existence within the market of two types of purchasers, one of which (GP fundholder) appeared to get shorter waiting times for its patients than the other (HA). Fundholders also managed to hold down prescription costs relative to non-fundholders and were better able to generate surpluses on their budgets than HAs.

- GP purchasers and GP commissioners in their various forms did appear to generate some improvements in the responsiveness of providers. However, there was no evidence of any increase in choice for patients; and, although there were changes over the period in indicators of quality such as waiting lists and patient satisfaction surveys, it was difficult to attribute these specifically to the reforms.

- Accountability to central government for HAs was high; that for fundholders relatively low. Trusts were accountable to purchasers, but did not seem to have become more accountable to their local populations.

- Overall, despite some changes in culture, measurable changes were small and perhaps not as great as was predicted (or feared). This was partly because competition within the market was limited, and this in turn may have been because the essential conditions for a market to operate were not fulfilled. More specifically, the incentives for the relevant agents were too weak and the constraints imposed by central government were too strong. This interpretation is reinforced by the fact that the area where there was the largest measurable change, GP fundholding, was one where the incentives were greatest and the constraints weakest.

● Lessons to be learned include the importance of devolving purchasing to GP-led groups. This is recognised in the Labour Government's proposals for 'replacing the internal market', especially those relating to the formation and development of PCGs. The proposals also include some welcome improvements in the incentive structures for trusts and purchasers. However, there is a potential for concern over the imposition of yet stronger central government constraints through the establishment of a performance framework and its monitoring institutions.

Part IV: **Appendices**

Appendix 1: Research evidence on health authority purchasing

0Reference	Study type*	Topic	Main findings
Appleby (1994a)	RM	Survey of 45 HA contracts in England	• The number of contracts and their complexity had increased over the first 3 years of the reforms. • There has been little change in the way HAs as a whole have allocated their budgets between services.
Appleby et al. (1994)	OS	Survey of purchasers in the West Midlands on attitudes to the reforms	• Most purchasers thought the purchaser/provider split a good thing. • Most purchasers believed that assessment of needs would result in changes to their purchasing intentions.
Audit Commission (1997)	CC	Purchasing specialised services	• HA information on service quality is poor. • Not clear whether HAs have reduced inequities of access to services. • Concluded that HAs are still probably best placed to purchase specialised services.
Carruthers et al. (1995)	CS	Development of purchasing in 3 HAs	• HAs have been effective in tackling weaknesses in service delivery and using their resources to increase efficiency and raise standards.
Flynn et al. (1995)	IR	Review of contracting for community health services	• Argues that the internal market undermines other objectives of HAs such as pursuing inter-agency collaboration.
Francombe (1991)	OS	National survey of HA DPHs on the principles of the NHS	• Majority of DPH doctors felt the reforms had changed the basic principles of the NHS. • Purchaser/provider split welcomed. • No change in quality. • Some improvements in waiting times. • Patient choice deteriorated. • No change in clinical freedom.
Frater and Dixon (1994)	RM	National survey of purchasers' use of outcome measurements in contracting	• Health outcomes were measured in at least some of the contracts of more than 60% of HAs surveyed but were formally linked to financial arrangements in less than 20%.

* For acronyms, see Abbreviations on page viii

Freemantle et al. (1993)	CS	Examined the developments of health care commissioning within 8 purchasing organisations	• Mixed findings on whether contracts have been placed to actually influence the pattern of care. • Weighted capitation formula has the most important influence upon the strength of the purchasing function within the internal market.
Ghodse (1995)	CS	Study of ECR referrals in one HA	• ECRs expose HAs to a significant degree of risk and may undermine commissioning strategies.
Gill (1993)	AE	Quality in purchasing	• No evidence that HAs are incorporating meaningful quality indicators in contracts.
Ham and Shapiro (1995)	CS	Review of experience of integrated purchasing between HAs and FHSAs	• Evidence of improvements in specific services. • The local context was important to the success of such schemes.
House of Commons Health Committee (1995a)	RM	Evidence submitted to Select Committee on Health on purchasers' shifts in priorities	• HAs have not made extensive shifts in the pattern of resources and have instead tended to concentrate on setting priorities at the margin.
House of Commons Health Committee (1994b)	OS	Evidence submitted to the House of Commons Select Committee on Health on RHA views of the costs and prospects of the internal market	• Most RHAs said it was impossible to achieve direct comparisons devoted to administration before and after the reforms. • RHAs could quote many examples of innovation in the field of priority setting.
Hudson and Willis (1995) Hudson (1996)	CS	Investigation into the approach to joint commissioning in 4 different localities in the Northern region	• Success depended on local circumstances rather than precise prescription. • Case studies found no clear way of engaging with GPs in the commissioning process. • Providers still held most of the power with which to shape the joint commissioning agenda.
Hughes et al. (1997)	CS/IR	NHS contracting in Wales	• Concluded that the development of NHS contracting policy is characterised by periodic strategic shifts which cast doubt on the theory that quasi-markets independently 'evolve'.

Jones *et al.* (1994)	PBA	Study of community health services for elderly people in 3 HAs in South Wales	• Found no increase in patient choice between 1990 and 1992.
Kirkup and Donaldson (1994)	IR	Review of purchasing	• Information asymmetries between providers and purchasers have prevented effective purchasing. • Because relatively small shifts in contracts can affect the overall viability of a provider, purchasers may be reluctant to make big changes in purchasing intentions.
Klein and Redmayne (1992)	IR	National survey of purchasing policies	• Purchasers were not explicitly rationing or providing evidence for the basis of their purchasing decisions. • HAs are attempting to engage GPs in the purchasing process.
Layzell (1994)	AE	Incorporating local views into purchasing	• Some limited progress has been made in responding to the views of local people.
Light (1994)	AE	Review of integrated purchasing from an international perspective	• The introduction of trusts and GP fundholders has conflicted with the goal of merging budgets. • True integrated purchasing requires large start-up funds and a breakdown of cultural barriers.
Ludlam *et al.* (1997)	AE	Equity of access to treatment for haemophilia	• Treatment decided by patient's postcode rather than need.
Majeed *et al.* (1994)	IR	Review of purchasers' use of routine data to monitor equity in primary and secondary care	• Evidence suggests that the reforms have not yet stimulated HAs routinely to monitor the equity implications of their purchasing decisions.
Marks (1995)	OS	Follow-up national survey of DPHs on the objectives of the NHS	• 56% of DPHs thought that equity considerations had been weakened. • No overall conclusion on whether the NHS was providing a comprehensive service. • 69% of DPHs thought that the NHS was meeting the needs of the population.

Maynard and Bloor (1996)	IR	Review of the purchasing function	• Purchasing function remains undeveloped. • Purchasers have been cautious in implementing evidence-based data into contracts.
McKee and Clarke (1995)	AE 1995	Review of guidelines and protocols in purchasing	• Purchasers' guidelines and protocols are limited in the extent to which they can deliver more effective care.
Millar (1997)	CS	Reports on work by Jenny Griffiths on HA and GP purchaser transactions costs	• Costs of supporting two partially intersecting commissioning systems is high. • HAs spend marginally less per capita on contracting than GP purchasers.
Moore and Dalziel (1993)	CS	The effects of the internal market on local ophthalmology services	• The internal market cannot always deliver a satisfactory and appropriate level of services unaided.
NHS Consultants' Association Health Policy Network (1995)	AE	Consultants' review of the NHS market	• Strategic planning is incompatible with an internal market. • Commercial confidentiality exists at the expense of cooperation and accountability between purchasers and providers. • The internal market has doubled the administrative running costs of the NHS.
Paton (1995)	IR/ OS	Based on interviews with managers in the NHS on the purchaser/provider split	• Purchasers avoid accountability of their rationing decisions by 'passing the buck' to providers. • Management costs must inevitably increase as contracts become more sophisticated. • Disaggregated purchasing leads to uncertainty in hospitals and a fragmented NHS as well as perverse incentives.
Pickard et al. (1995)	CS	The role of local people in informing the assessment of health needs in 3 HAs	• Despite a commitment to involving local people, HAs are still not clear about how to actually achieve it.
Raftery et al. (1994)	RM	Survey of HA contracts	• HAs have employed more detailed contracts since the start of the reforms. • HAs claimed the purchaser efficiency index encouraged a bias towards acute activity.

Redmayne et al. (1993)	CC	Analysis of HAs' spending priorities	<ul><li>There is evidence of a shift of resources towards primary and community care.</li><li>Services for elderly, mentally ill and people with learning disabilities have suffered.</li><li>Little evidence that decisions are made on the grounds of effectiveness.</li><li>Purchasers are not examining variations in the distribution of budgets among different services and client groups.</li></ul>
Redmayne (1995)	CS	Analysis of HAs' 5-year spending plans	<ul><li>Equity and accessibility are the dominant values guiding HAs' 5-year plans.</li><li>60% of plans include equality of access and 42% include the provision of equitable services.</li></ul>
Redmayne (1996)	CS	Analysis of HAs' spending priorities	<ul><li>Purchasers are experimenting with a number of ways of gaining the public's input into priority setting with limited success.</li><li>Explicit rationing is on the increase.</li></ul>
Roberts (1993)	IR	Managing the internal market	<ul><li>Annual cycles of contracting are inappropriate for long-term planning.</li><li>Purchasing is under-regulated and it is not clear if purchasers are ultimately accountable to the government, the HA or the public.</li></ul>
Shapiro (1994)	CS	Examined collaboration between HAs and smaller purchaser groupings in England and Scotland	<ul><li>Organisations that collaborate seemed more likely to achieve their stated objectives.</li><li>Locality models which relate to GPs seem to be effective for collaborative work with both non-fundholding GPs and fundholders.</li></ul>
Sheldon and Borowitz (1993)	AE	Review of purchaser measures of quality in the NHS	<ul><li>Simply measuring activity is not enough to assess quality and performance.</li><li>Most contracts did not specify what is meant by quality and how it will be measured.</li><li>Purchasers are unable to reward appropriate treatment such as 'watchful waiting' because it results in no activity.</li></ul>
Walsh (1995)	AE	Review of the NHS reforms	<ul><li>HAs are not truly representative.</li><li>No evidence of improved responsiveness or efficiency.</li></ul>

Appendix 2: Research evidence on General Practitioner Fundholding

Reference	Study type*	Topic	Main findings
Association of CHCs for England and Wales (1994)	OS/ AE	Access to care	• Concludes that there is strong evidence to suggest that patients of fundholders (FHs) get better access to hospital treatments.
Association of CHCs for England and Wales (1995)	AE	Accountability procedures	• Argued that accountability measures need to be improved.
Abel-Smith (1995)	AE	NHS reforms	• FH has created a two-tier system yet FH is clearest evidence of success because FHs get better deals for their patients.
Armstrong et al. (1991)	OS	GP referrals in Bromley, Kent	• Pressure by patients for referrals appears to explain some of variation in GP referral patterns.
Audit Commission (1995b)	RM	National survey of FH practices, late summer 1994	• FHs more common in suburbs and shires than in cities. • £65m underspend by FH practices overall. • Only 3% of FHs overspent their budgets.
Audit Commission (1996)	RM	National study of GP FHs: questionnaire survey of all first to 5th-wave FHs: response rate 5%	• FH has made little overall change to delivery of services. • No evidence that FH prescribe more economically. • Accountability and audit poor. • 1 in 5 FH overspent in 1993/4. • Costs of staff, equipment and computing for FH estimated at £232m. Underspends £206m. • High transactions costs for providers. • Improved GP–provider communications. • More on-site services.
Bailey et al. (1993)	RM	Outreach clinics in England and Wales	• More specialist activity in FH than non-FH practices. • Little interaction between GP and specialist has resulted.
Bain (1991) Bain (1992)	CS	FH in Calverton, Trent	• FH has high demands on staff time. • Efficiency gains and waiting times improved. • Budget holding decreases barriers for change.

* For acronyms, see Abbreviations on page viii

Bain (1993)	CS	Prescribing in Calverton, Trent	• FH has lowered cost of prescribing through greater use of generic and reduced repeat prescribing.
Bradlow and Coulter (1993)	CBA	Prescribing costs in Oxford Region: 8 FH practices, 7 non-FH practices	• FHs have curbed increase in prescribing costs more effectively than non-FHs.
Burr et al. (1992)	CBA	Prescribing patterns in mid-Glamorgan: 4 FH and 4 non-FH practices	• Drug expenditure increased 2.4% in FH practices and 7.5% in non-FH practices. • FHs make greater use of generic drugs.
Consumers' Association patients. (1995a)	OS	GP views on FH nation-wide: 1017 non-FHs and 679 FH GPs	• Strong belief that two-tier system exists. • Quicker access to hospital care for FH. • Extra services provided on-site.
Consumers' Association (1995b)	OS	Patients' views on FH: 1618 patients interviewed	• Patients of FHs less satisfied with services received than patients of non-FHs.
Cornell (1996)	IR	Effect of FH on patient care	• FHs gain process advantages and greater amount of practice-based care. • Improved quality in contracts and reduced waiting times. • Reduction in doctor–patient trust. • Growth in transactions costs. • Cream skimming did occur. • Two-tierism present. • Funding has not been equitable. • Lack of research – particularly with comparison to other models of purchasing.
Corney (1994)	OS	FHs in SE Thames RHA	• Greater responsiveness of providers to demands by fundholders.
Coulter (1995a)	IR	Review of FH literature	• Claims that FHs have improved efficiency, responsiveness and quality of care is not supported by the evidence.
Coulter (1995b)	AE	Shifting balance from secondary to primary care	• Primary care may not be an acceptable substitute for secondary care.
Coulter (1995c)	IR	Review of evidence on FH	• There is a need for well funded, co-ordinated research on risks, costs and benefits of FH compared to other models of care purchasing.

Coulter and Bradlow (1993)	CBA	Referrals in Oxford region: 10 FH practices and 6 non-FH practices	• Referral patterns largely unchanged. No evidence of shift from specialist to GP care.
Dixon and Glennerster (1995)	IR	Review of FH literature	• FHs have curbed prescribing costs, given leverage to improve hospital services, reduced waiting times. • FHs may receive more money than non-FHs. • Impact on quality, equity and transactions costs unknown.
Dixon *et al.* (1994)	HC	Distribution of funds between non-FH and FH practices in NW Thames RHA	• FH practices seem to have been funded more generously than non-FH practices.
Dowell *et al.* (1995)	CS	Prescribing changes in one FH practice in Scotland	• Mean cost per day's treatment fell by 9.4%. • Volume of treatment fell by 10.7%. • Generic prescribing rose from 30 to 50%.
Dowling (1997)	HC/ RM	Effect of FH on waiting times in West Sussex	• Patients of FH practices had shorter waiting times than those of non-FHs.
Ellwood (1997)	CS	Influence of price and quality on 35 GP FH referral patterns in the West Midlands	• Few changes in referral patterns even though the potential savings from changing were high.
Fear and Cattell (1994)	HC	Referrals in community old age psychiatry in South and East Clwyd: 185 GPs of which 88 became FHs	• Overall pattern of referrals unchanged. • Significant decrease in domiciliary consultations requested by FH GPs suggest shortfall in number of referrals.
Fisher (1993)	AE	Equity of access	• FH patients receive preferential treatment.
Glennerster (1994)	IR	Review of FH evidence	• Tangible efficiency gains by leverage of hospitals and practice innovations offset by poor budget allocation mechanism. • Justifiable fears of equity losses. • Accountability poor.

Glennerster et al. (1994a, 1994b)	PBA	Various reform issues in nation-wide sample: 10 1st-wave, one 2nd-wave and 16 3rd-wave FHs	• Tangible efficiency gains by leverage on hospitals and practice innovations offset by poor budget allocation mechanism. • Justifiable fears of equity losses.
Gosden and Torgerson (1997)	IR	Review of literature on FH prescribing and referrals	• No evidence to suggest that prospective FHs inflated costs prior to FH. • FHs constrain rise in prescribing and referrals more successfully than non-FHs. • Early FHs had high referral rates and used less generic drugs. Hence their ability to contain prescribing costs enhanced.
Harris and Scrivener (1996)	HC	Prescribing costs at all general practices in England	• Absolute prescribing costs increased over the first 5 years of fundholding, by 66% in non-FHs and by 56–59% for FHs. • Most of the reduction in the rate of increase for FHs was obtained in the first year of FH. • After the 3rd year, the rate of increase was the same for both FHs and non-FHs.
Healey and Reid (1994)	HC	Prescribing costs and referrals in Grampian Health Board: all 88 practices of which 6 1st-wave FHs, 16 2nd-wave FHs and 64 non-FHs	• No significant difference in prescribing costs in pre- and post-reform periods for all FH and non-FH practices. • FH outpatient referrals decreased by 7%. • Evidence that FH practices delayed cost containment measures in pre-FH period to gain greater drug budget allocation.
Heaney et al. (1994)	PBA	Referrals in 6 FH groups in Scotland	• Reduction in outpatient referrals. • Referral allocation leading to inequity due to historical cost basis.
Hoey (1995)	IR/ OS	Review of FH literature and survey of FH and non-FH GPs	• The system discriminates against non-FH patients. FHs out of touch with patient views.
Howie et al. (1993)	PBA	Prescribing in 6 FH groups in Scotland	• FH prescribing has remained stable. • Little change to outpatient referrals. • Patient satisfaction reduced slightly.
Howie et al. (1994)	PBA	Quality of care and prescribing in 6 FH groups in Scotland	• Pain relief prescriptions remained steady over the study period. • Referrals for joint pain fell significantly. • Quality of care for patients with pain had been maintained in terms of consultation time.

Howie et al. (1995a)	PBA	Prescribing, referrals, clinical care, administration and perceptions of cost and benefit in 6 FH groups in Scotland	• Prescribing volume has reduced and the quality maintained. • Little change in referral activity. Downward trend matched by upward trend in use of direct-access services. • Clinical care of patients has remained stable. • Shift of ownership of care to primary level has been beneficial to GPs and patients. • Patients remain generally satisfied over period. • Lead doctors perceptions of benefits higher than non-lead doctors.
Howie et al. (1995b)	PBA	Quality of care for patients in 6 FH groups in Scotland	• Consultation lengths remained constant overall. • Benefits to some patients may have been matched by disadvantage to other groups.
Kammerling and Kinnear (1996)	CC	Referral rates in 10 FH practices and 22 control practices in one HA	• FH patients referred more quickly than non-FH patients. • Some hospitals provide clinics especially for FH patients.
Kerrison and Corney (1998)	CS	Private provision of outreach clinics in FH practices	• Considerable private provision of FHs' outreach clinics. • No system to monitor the impact of this on the quality and cost of services provided.
Kind et al. (1992)	OS	GP views of FH in Yorkshire region: 364 GPs of which 34 1st-wave, 20 2nd-wave, 65 preparing for 3rd-wave, 243 non-FHs	• Two-tier system not justified in terms of waiting times for hospital consultations. • Quality of services advanced in terms of more practice-based services. This may be more due to GP contract than to FH.
Kind et al. (1993a)	HC	Prescribing in Yorkshire Region: 101 practices. 21 1st-wave fundholders	• Practice type does not seem to explain variation between practices in prescribing. The location of the practice is of greater significance.
Kind et al. (1993b)	OS	Patients views on FH in Yorkshire region: 417 FH patients and 166 non-FH patients	• 80% patients did not know whether their practice was an FH practice or not.
Leese and Bosanquet (1996)	OS	GP views on fundholding in 6 GP FHSAs in different locality types	• GPs dissatisfied with level of workload and administration. • 38% of GPs said general practice had improved since 1990 GP contract.

Luxton (1993)	AE	Equity of access	• FH patients receive preferential treatments.
Macrae Todd (1993)	AE	Outreach clinics	• FH ask for practitioners to undertake outreach clinics.
Mahon et al. (1994)	OS	Patient choice for hospital	• Survey of patients before and after FH (about 300 in each case). • Level of patient choice for hospital remains low – reforms have had little impact.
Marks (1995)	OS	Survey of DPHs, April 1994.	• 28% ($n = 121$) commented that FH scheme had deleterious effects on two-tier system. Also a reduction in patient–doctor trust.
Marwick (1994)	IR	Review of FH for New Zealand Government	• FH practices get quicker and easier access to secondary services. • FH practices have more on-site services. • FH able to reduce growth in prescribing costs more effectively than non-FHs. • No evidence of poorer outcomes, reduced quality or reduced patient satisfaction.
Maxwell et al. (1993)	HC	Prescribing patterns in Scotland: comparison of 6 FH groups and 6 non-FH groups	• Both FH and non-FH practices reduced drug volumes prescribed. • Costs rose less in FH than in non-FH practices.
Maynard and Bloor (1996)	IR	Aspects of the NHS reforms	• Rise in prescribing costs has been short term. • FH has diversified practice-based services but this may not be cost-effective. • FH studies are mainly descriptive and do not use adequate controls. • Consensus that FHs gain better process efficiency from providers.
McAvoy (1993)	AE	Observation of events in 6 practices: 4 FH and 2 non-FH	• First-wave FH more dynamic. • 'Spectacular' changes in services for FH patients. • Polarisation of FH and non-FH practices.
McCullough (1993)	AE	Equity of access	• FH patients get preferential treatment.
Milhil (1993)	AE	Equity of access	• Two-tier system supported by Government.

National Audit Office (1994)	RM	Audit of FH scheme: 110 1st-wave and 110 2nd-wave	• FH report success in reducing waiting times, getting a more responsive service and additional practice-based services. • FH make more use of generics and increase in drug costs lower than in non-FHs. • Accountability could be enhanced by more rigorous evaluation. • Budget setting inaccurate – need for national methodology. • Little consultation between FH and HA over purchasing intentions.
Newton *et al.* (1993)	OS	Review of fundholding in Northern Region: 19 GPs in 10 FH practices	• Greater responsiveness of hospital consultants. • No change in patient choice. • Extra staff taken on and high administration time. • Uncertainty of making savings year on year.
Peeke (1993)	CC	Waiting times in Oxford region	• No significant difference in the waiting times for hospital treatment between FH and non-FH patients.
Penhale *et al.* (1993)	CC	Prescribing costs: 118 non-FHs and 20 FHs	• Mean number of asthma and total prescriptions were lower in FH practices by 15% and 8.4% respectively.
Pennington (1995)	AE	Transactions costs in Nottingham	• Nottingham Non-FH Group claim that costs for running as a non-FH over £3m a year less than if they went for FH.
Petchey (1993)	IR	Review of first year of FH	• Claims of increased efficiency hard to substantiate. • Fundholders budgets seem over-allocated.
Petchey (1995)	IR	Review of fund-holding literature	• Few reliable conclusions about FH can be drawn from existing research.
Purchasing in Practice (1995)	IR	Review of literature on FH prescribing	• FH has helped to hold back increases in prescribing costs. • FHs may be more cautious about adopting new and/or more expensive drugs.
Rafferty *et al.* (1997)	HC	Prescribing patterns in Northern Ireland; 23 1st-wave FHs, 34 2nd-wave FHs, 9 3rd-wave FHs and 268 non-FHs	• Prescribing costs increased throughout the study. • Among the FHs the rate of increase in costs after FH was lower than among non-FHs.

Robinson (1996)	HC	Prescribing in Avon: 156 GPs	• First-wave FH spent less on drugs prior to FH. • Second-wave FH practices were highest spending group on prescriptions. • No significant difference in rate of increase between FH and non-FH practices. • First-wave FHs unable to sustain reduction in cost growth after initial period.
Samuel (1992)	AE	Equity of access	• FH patients receive preferential treatments.
South Bucks CHC (1994)	RM	GP referral rates in South Bucks: 54 patients of which 24 FH, 30 non-FH	• Waiting time for orthopaedic operations 12 months longer for non-FH patients. • Gynaecology referrals for appointment longer for non-FHs although operating waiting times the same.
Stewart-Brown et al. (1995)	CBA	Prescribing patterns in Oxford region: 8 1st-wave FH practices and 5 non-FH practices	• Early success of FH in curbing prescribing costs have not been borne out over the longer period.
Surender et al. (1995)	CBA	Referral patterns in Oxford region: 10 FH practices and 6 non-FH practices	• No significant fall in referral rates. • GPs may have inflated referral rates in preparatory year.
Timmins (1995b)	AE	Inappropriate use of savings	• FH practice sets up on-site shop for income generation.
Toth et al. (1997)	HC	Impact on emergency referrals: 21 FH practices and 521 non-FH	• No evidence that FH had an impact on the proportion of emergency admissions.
Trimble and Black (1996)	HC	Prescribing in Nottingham: FH and non-FH practices in entire Nottingham district	• FHs make initial savings but their costs of prescribing are now higher, and rising more rapidly, than non-FHs. • Reduction in costs very small compared to overall costs. • Nottingham Non-FH Group reduce rise in costs more effectively through linked prescribing and purchasing budget at district level.
Whynes et al. (1995)	HC	Prescribing costs in Lincolnshire: 19 FHs, 86 non-FHs	• FHs were more successful in meeting drug budget targets than non-FHs.

Wilson et al. (1995)	HC	Prescribing in Mersey RHA: 100 FHs and 312 non-FHs	• FHs have reduced rate of increase in prescribing costs compared to non-FHs and increased use of generics.
Wilson and Walley (1995)	HC	Prescribing costs	• The earlier difference in prescribing has not been maintained since dramatic rise in use of generics by non-FHs. • FHs still contain costs more effectively than non-FHs.
Wisely (1993)	AE	FH experiences in Grampian	• Describes own experiences with 6 shadow FHs. • Quality changes are possible through negotiation with hospitals.
Wright (1994)	OS	FH GPs in Yorkshire RHA: 9 FH lead GPs interviewed	• Perceived improvement to relationship with provider units and their consultants.

Appendix 3: Research evidence on locality and general practitioner commissioning

Reference	Study type*	Topic	Main findings
Balogh (1996)	IR	Review of the literature on locality purchasing	• Documented progress of purchasing mainly limited to operational issues in the first 2 years of the reforms. • Successful locality commissioning dependent on policy context and existing relationships between key stakeholders.
Balogh & Thomasson (1995)	CS	Locality commissioning in Northumberland	• Pressures over agreeing contracts meant that locality GPs' lists of priorities remained unfulfilled. • Without additional resources, achievements could only be made in marginal ways.
Black et al. (1994)	CS 1994	Non-FH in Nottingham	• As a large purchaser but with low management costs the group claimed to have secured access to quality secondary care without incurring inequity of access. • Many of the benefits of GP fundholding (responsiveness, choice and quality) could be achieved without joining the scheme.
British Medical Association (1997)	OS	GP involvement in the commissioning	• 69% of LMCs compared to 45% of HAs thought that GPs had a positive impact on process HA purchasing.
Crail (1997)	IR	Locality commissioning simulation exercise	• Revealed a conflict of interest for GPs between their roles as commissioners and providers of services. • Danger that conflicting commissioning decisions by different groups will act against the public/patient interest.
Dixon et al. (1996)	CS	GP commissioning	• Significant improvements were achieved in waiting times and their management costs were approximately half as great as those of FHs.

* For acronyms, see Abbreviations on page viii

Eve and Hodgkin (1991)	CS	Pilot study of 8 non-FHs who sought to collaborate in monitoring quality of care	• Monitoring of quality by GPs is likely to provide an independent source of objective, valid information, without the need for FH.
Freake et al. (1997)	CS	Involving local community groups in locality commissioning in Newcastle	• Involving patients in locality commissioning has led to the identification of locally relevant priority areas.
Glennerster et al. (1996)	CC	Comparison of fundholding with alternative HA-led purchasing models	• FH more successful then non-FH in solving problems they had identified. • Non-FH less likely to push for change if benefits did not accrue to whole area. • Those non-FH schemes which most resembled FH were the most successful.
Graffy and Williams (1994)	OS	GP participation in an HA's purchasing forum in Hackney	• Most GPs and managers thought that the forum was responsive. • 75% of quality targets and 55% of service developments were contributed to by GPs.
Ham (1992a) Ham (1992b)	CS	Review of 6 locality purchasing projects around the country	• Data requirements were considerable. • Complicated to devolve budgets equitably. • Lack of infrastructure to support schemes.
Hine & Bachmann (1997)	CS	Locality commissioning in Avon	• 20 initiatives were identified that had changed services to patients. • Locality commissioning had selectively changed services with limited extra funding.
Hudson-Hart et al. (1997)	CS	Locality commissioning	• GPs appeared to have had more of an advisory and informative role rather than being directly responsible for purchasing.
Jankowski et al. (1997)	CS	GP involvement in locality commissioning	• Most of the benefits reported were in primary and community services. • Some GPs reluctant to take on extra work. • Lack of clarity about what locality commissioning was trying to achieve.
London Health Economics Consortium (1996)	IR	The influence of GP commissioning and FH on innovation in the NHS	• No clear difference between FH and GP commissioning in terms of innovation. • HAs appear to be the best adapted to promoting innovation.

Murray (1993)	IR	Literature review of alternative models of locality commissioning	• Locality commissioning appears to provide a more sustainable basis on which to involve GPs closely without the need for FH.
Office for Public Management (1994)	CS	Evaluation of a locality purchasing scheme in London	• Savings were achieved for the same level of activity. • Specific service gaps filled. • Improved access to some services. • Only limited GP participation.
Pickin and Popay (1994)	CS	Review of locality purchasing schemes in England	• No obvious relationship between the level of costs and benefits between different schemes. • Locality commissioning seemed to improve integration between primary and secondary care.
Primary Care Support Force (1996)	CS	GP involvement in commissioning	• GPs complained that despite clear evidence of the potential benefits of changing provider, HAs were unwilling to move contracts. • Only 39% of GPs felt they had a role in making decisions. • Less than a third of GPs believed their involvement led to greater responsiveness to patients/public. • Mixed views on how accountable GP groups were to the public and HAs. • GPs rated liaison with providers as the most effective model of involving GPs in commissioning. • GP involvement ended unnecessary duplication of some services.
Salfield (1997)	AE	Locality commissioning	• Locality commissioning may be a way to ensure equity, if budgets are set fairly.
Shapiro *et al.* (1996)	CS	GPs involvement in commissioning	• The form and style of HA leadership was considered vital to the effective relationship between GPs and HAs.
Smith *et al.* (1997a)	CS	Primary care led commissioning and provision in the West Midlands	• Fieldwork revealed a vast array of initiatives with primary care. • Diversity is to be encouraged in the absence of definite evidence on the benefits or otherwise of various schemes.
Smith & Shapiro (1996) Smith & Shapiro (1997)	CS	Evaluation of locality commissioning in County Durham	• There were achievements in terms of service changes and the development of new relationships and alliances. • There was some evidence of localities seeking the views of patients on a local basis in planning services.

Wainwright (1996)	IR	GP commissioning	• The existence of localities should not exclude the possibility of district-wide service reviews and strategic planning.
Willis (1996)	CS/ IR	Evaluation of 4 GP commissioning groups	• Participants claimed that GP commissioning was 'cost-effective' and brought about significant quality improvements. • However, it is unclear how cost-effectiveness was measured.

Appendix 4: Research evidence on total purchasing

Reference	Study type*	Topic	Main findings
Baxter et al. (1998)	CS	Budgetary and risk management of TPPs	• Most TPPs were able to keep within budget.
Bevan et al. (1998)	CS	Budgetary and risk management of TPPs	• Most TPPs were able to keep their spending within budget. • However, only one third had agreed protocols for modifying spending within budget.
Dixon et al. (1998)	CS	Accountability framework for TPPs	• Loose informal framework of accountability. • TPPs have focused most on financial accountability.
Harrison (1997b)	CS	One TPP in West Yorkshire	• The TPP has tended to concentrate attention on maintaining local acute services.
Mahon et al. (1998)	CS	How TPPs inform themselves for purchasing	• Poor activity and cost data have hampered many TPPs' attempts to change services.
Mays, et al. (1998a)	CS	Management costs of TPPs	• Direct management costs associated with total purchasing in the first live year varied from £0.02 to £6.97 per capita. • Larger TPPs are more costly in total to manage but multi-practice TPPs are no more costly to manage per capita than single practice TPPs.
Mays et al. (1998b)	CS	Achievements of 1st-wave TPPs in their first live year	• 82% of TPPs achieved their objectives in relation to developing primary care but only 33% achieved mental health objectives.
Newbronner (1996)	CS	Doncaster Primary Care 2000 project	• Transactions costs of the project were relatively high. • None of the GPs involved in the project believed that TP would prevent them from accepting potentially expensive patients onto their lists. • Possibility of fragmentation in planning and provision because not all GPs in the area were part of TP.
Raftery & McLeod (1998)	CS/ CC	Total purchasing and hospital activity changes	• Evidence from 11 TPPs to suggest that TPPs have made progress in reducing the number of occupied bed days.

* For acronyms, see Abbreviations on page viii

Robinson et al. (1998)	CS	TPP contracting	• 30% of 1st wave TPPs did not take control of a budget in 1996/7.
Total Purchasing National Evaluation Team (1997)	CS/ CC	National Evaluation of Total Purchasing: preparatory year	• The costs of the preparatory year of TP ranged from £0.26 to £8.05 per capita; both lower than the fundholding average. • Limited evidence to date on whether quality of services has improved. • Limited evidence of a strong accountability framework other than for financial accountability.
Walsh (1997)	CS/ CC	Berkshire Integrated Purchasing Project	• Little evidence of service efficiency to date. • Some evidence that patient satisfaction among TPP patients higher than comparator patients.

Appendix 5: Research evidence on trusts

Reference	Study type*	Topic	Main findings
Adams (1995)	CS	Financial regime	• Financial regime contains perverse incentives which punish efficient providers.
Appleby (1995)	RM	Management costs	• The absolute increase in NHS senior managers between 1987 and 1991 was as great as that between 1991 and 1994.
Appleby and Little (1992)	IR	Cost-Weighted Activity Index (CWAI)	• CWAI fails to include any activity not counted in Korner statistics which acts as a disincentive to innovation. • Accuracy of raw data used in its calculation is questionable. • Calculations of finance distorted by inclusion of non-recurrent funding.
Appleby et al. (1994)	PBA	Managed competition	• Conditions existed for competition to take place in 1991/92.
Ashburner (1994)	OS	Accountability	• A large proportion of trust non-executives have a business background. • Over half have had recent involvement with the voluntary sector. • There was significant under-representation of minority ethnic groups.
Association of CHCs of England and Wales (1989)	AE	Accountability	• Trust boards threaten accountability. • The solution is to have CHC representatives on trust boards.
Association of CHCs of England and Wales (1994)	AE	Two-tierism	• Gave several examples of trusts having preferential access policies for GP FHs.
Audit Commission (1995)	IR/ RM	Management costs	• Defining what should be counted as a management cost is not straightforward because the cost of managers is not the same as the cost of management.

* For acronyms, see Abbreviations on page viii

Bartlett and Le Grand (1992, 1994a, 1994b)	CC	Trust unit costs	• Trusts have lower costs than DMUs, but: first-wave trusts were a self-selected group with lower costs prior to trust status and second-wave trusts have lower costs due to case mix, size, patient flow and location.
Caines (1994)	AE	Trust freedoms	• Trusts have had their proposed freedoms curtailed and this has limited their effectiveness.
Centre for the Evaluation of Public Policy and Practice (1995)	CC	Trust freedoms compared to housing associations and grant-maintained schools	• Trusts have had fewer freedoms than grant-maintained schools or housing associations.
Clarke and McKee (1992)	IR	FCEs	• FCEs have a tendency to inflate activity.
Clinical Standards Advisory Groups (1993–1995)	CC/ RM/ CS	Quality of care for specific services	• DMUs generally admit patients through A&E slightly quicker than trusts. • Good providers of services for schizophrenia tend to be found in the same areas as good purchasers.
Francombe (1996)	OS	Two-tierism	• 88% of London doctors believe FHs get better treatment from trusts.
Government Statistical Service (1994, 1995)	RM	Management costs	• Increase in management costs more due to reclassification of existing clinical posts than an increase in bureaucracy associated with the creation of the internal market.
Ham (1991b)	IR	Accountability and privatisation	• Trusts are symbolic of a blurring of boundaries between public and private sectors.
Labour Party (1992)	AE	Accountability	• The Conservatives have filled trust boards with their supporters.
Labour Party (1994)	AE	Management costs	• Expenditure on managers' cars rose 350% after the introduction of the internal market.
Marks (1995)	OS	Quality of care	• A majority of DPHs felt that services had improved following the introduction of trusts.

Moonie and Galbraith (1989)	IR	Management costs	• Expenditure on bureaucracy likely to increase as a result of the internal market.
NHS Executive (1994c, 1995)	RM	Activity levels	• More patients have been treated since the NHS reforms.
Propper (1995a)	IR	Managed competition	• Only 8% of acute providers had a monopoly of general surgery, orthopaedics, ENT and gynaecology inside a 30-mile radius. • Competition did not take place. • Bilateral monopolies between purchasers and providers formed.
Radical Statistics Health Group (1992a, 1992b, 1995)	RM	Activity levels	• Increase in FCEs fraudulently passed off as an increase in patients. • Increased FCEs part of longer term trend due to changes in medical practice rather than the reforms.
Seng *et al.* (1993)	IR	FCEs	• FCEs have a tendency to inflate activity.
Shaoul (1996)	RM/ IR	Financial regime	• Charging for capital has negative effects for choice, equity and quality.
Smee (1995)	RM	Introduction of efficient techniques and length of waiting time	• Trusts do not uniformly have higher day case rates than DMUs. • Trusts have not uniformly reduced waiting times quicker than DMUs.
Söderlund *et al.* (1997)	CBA	Trust unit costs	• Costs decreased with the change from directly managed to trust status. • Some hospitals may have been intentionally unproductive before becoming trusts so that large improvements could be shown on change of status.
Traynor (1995)	OS	Trust freedoms	• Trust managers have felt increased freedom to make decisions.
Wall (1994)	IR	Effect of trusts on efficiency and quality	• Administering the internal market would be likely to increase management costs. • Different trusts have conflicting incentives which may damage the continuity of patient care.

Bibliography

Abel-Smith B (1995) Health reform: old wine in new bottles. *Eurohealth* 1:7–9.

Adams CBT (1995) OxDONS syndrome: the inevitable disease of the NHS reforms (letter). *British Medical Journal* 311:1559–1560.

Appleby J (1994a) *Developing Contracting*. Birmingham: University of Birmingham, Health Services Management Centre, National Association of Health Authorities and Trusts.

Appleby J (1994b) Data briefing: waiting lists. *Health Service Journal* 104(5428):36–37.

Appleby J (1995) Managers: in the ascendancy. *Health Service Journal* 105(5471):32–33.

Appleby J, Little V (1993) Health and efficiency. *Health Service Journal* 103(5351): 20–22.

Appleby J, Sheldon T, Clarke A (1993) Run for your money. *Health Service Journal* 103(5355):22–24.

Appleby J, Smith P, Ranade W, Little V, Robinson R (1994) Monitoring managed competition. In: Le Grand J, Robinson R (Eds), *Evaluating the NHS Reforms*. London: King's Fund Institute, 24–53.

Armstrong D, Fry J, Armstrong P (1991) Doctors' perceptions of pressure from patients for referral. *British Medical Journal* 302:1186–1188.

Ashburner L (1994) The composition of NHS Trust Boards. *Health Services Management Research* 7:154–164.

Association of Community Health Councils for England and Wales (1989) *Working for Patients? The Patients' View*. London: Association of Community Health Councils for England and Wales.

Association of Community Health Councils for England and Wales (1994) *Fundholding and Access to Hospital Care.* London: Association of Community Health Councils for England and Wales.

Association of Community Health Councils for England and Wales (1995) *Accountability of Fundholding.* London: Association of Community Health Councils for England and Wales.

Atkinson C (1989) Donning a manager's cap. *Health Service Journal* 99: 1218–1219.

Audit Commission (1995a) *A Price on their Heads: Measuring Management Costs in NHS Trusts.* London: HMSO.

Audit Commission (1995b) *Briefing on GP Fundholding.* London: HMSO.

Audit Commission (1996) *What the Doctor Ordered: a Study of GP Fundholding in England and Wales.* London: HMSO.

Audit Commission (1997) *Higher Purchase: Commissioning Specialised Services in the NHS.* London: Audit Commission.

Bachmann M, Bevan G (1996) Determining the size of a total purchasing site to manage the financial risks of rare costly referrals. *British Medical Journal* 313:1054–1057.

Baeza J, Calnan M (1997) Implementing quality: a study of the adoption and implementation of quality standards in the contracting process in a general practitioner multifund. *Journal of Health Services Research and Policy* 2:205–211.

Bailey J, Black M, Wilkin D (1993) Specialist outreach clinics in general practices. *British Medical Journal* 308:1083–1086.

Bain J (1991) Budget holding: the first 150 days in Calverton. *British Medical Journal* 303: 907–908.

Bain J (1992) Budget holding in Calverton: one year on. *British Medical Journal* 304:971–973.

Bain J (1993) Budget-holding: here to stay? *British Medical Journal* 306: 1185–1188.

Baker D, Klein R (1991) Explaining outputs of primary health care: population and practice factors. *British Medical Journal* 303:225–229.

Balogh R (1996) Exploring the role of localities in health commissioning: a review of the literature. *Social Policy and Administration* 30:99–113.

Balogh R, Thomasson G (1995) The persuaders. *Health Service Journal* 105(5465):26.

Barr N, Glennerster H, Le Grand J (1989) Working for patients: the right approach? *Social Policy and Administration* 23:117–127.

Bartlett W, Le Grand J (1992) *The Impact of the NHS Reforms on Hospital Costs*. Bristol: School for Advanced Urban Studies, University of Bristol.

Bartlett W, Le Grand J (1994a) *Costs and Trusts. Studies in Decentralisation and Quasi-Markets 18*. Bristol: School for Advanced Urban Studies, University of Bristol.

Bartlett W, Le Grand J (1994b) The performance of Trusts. In: Robinson R, Le Grand J (Eds), *Evaluating the NHS Reforms*. London: King's Fund Institute, 54–73.

Baxter K, Bachmann M, Bevan G (1998) *Survey of Budgetary and Risk Management of Total Purchasing Pilot Projects 1996–97*. London: King's Fund.

Benady S, Barr F (1991) Moving your consultants into the surgery. *Fundholding* 1:28–29.

Ben-Shlomo Y, Chaturvedi N (1995) Assessing equity in access to health care provision in the UK: does where you live affect your chances of getting a coronary artery bypass graft? *Journal of Epidemiology and Community Health* 49:200–204.

Benzeval M, Judge K (1991) Health and healthcare in London. *Public Money and Management* Spring:25–32.

Bevan G, Baxter K, Bachmann M (1998) *Budgetary and Risk Management of Total Purchasing Pilot Projects*. National Evaluation of Total Purchasing Pilot Projects Working Paper. London: King's Fund.

Black DG, Birchall AD, Trimble IMG (1994) Non-fundholding in Nottingham: a vision of the future. *British Medical Journal* 309:930–932.

Boersma G (1996) Ours to reason why. *Health Service Journal* 106 (5524): 28–29.

Bowie C, Sturgeon R (1994) Commentary: better data needed for analysis. *British Medical Journal* 309:34.

Bowling A, Jacobson B, Southgate L, Formby J (1991) General practitioners' views on quality specifications for outpatient referrals and core contracts. *British Medical Journal* 303:292–294.

Bradlow J, Coulter A (1993) Effect of fundholding and indicative prescribing schemes on general practitioner prescribing costs. *British Medical Journal* 307:1186–1189.

Brazier J, Hutton J, Jeavons R (1990) Evaluating the reform of the NHS. In: Culyer A, Maynard A, Posnett J (Eds), *Competition in Health Care: Reforming the NHS*. London: Macmillan, 216–236.

British Medical Association (1994) *Accountability in the NHS: a Discussion Paper*. London: British Medical Association.

British Medical Association (1997) *Medical Involvement in the Commissioning Process: a Report of a National Study of Health Authorities and LMCs in England*. London: British Medical Association.

Broadbent J, Laughlin R (1997) Contractual changes in schools and general practices: professional resistance and the role of absorption and absorbing groups. In: Flynn R, Williams G (Eds), *Contracting for Health: Quasi-markets and the National Health Service*. Oxford: Oxford University Press, 30–46.

Brogan S (1993) Who says fundholders are loaded? *Health Service Journal* 103(5342):22.

Burr A, Walker R, Stent S (1992) Impact of fundholding on general practices' prescribing patterns. *The Pharmaceutical Journal* 249, supplement No. 8.

Butler J (1992) *Patients, Policies and Politics: before and after Working for Patients*, Buckingham: Open University Press.

Butler P (1996) Supermodels: the vital statistics. *Health Service Journal* 106(5489):12–13.

Caines E (1994) Impact of trusts on the management of the NHS. *Health Services Management Research* 7:181–186.

Carruthers I, Fillingham D, Ham C, James J (1995) *Purchasing in the NHS: the Story so Far*. Birmingham: Health Services Management Centre, University of Birmingham.

Centre for the Evaluation of Public Policy and Practice (1995) *NHS Trusts, Grant Maintained Schools and Housing Associations*. Mimeo, Norwich: University of East Anglia.

Checkland P (1997) Rhetoric and reality in contracting: research in and on the National Health Service. In: Flynn R, Williams G (Eds), *Contracting for Health: Quasi-markets and the National Health Service*. Oxford: Oxford University Press, 115–134.

Clarke A, McKee M (1992) The consultant episode: an unhelpful measure. *British Medical Journal* 305:1307–1308.

Clarke A, McKee M, Appleby J, Sheldon TA (1993) Efficient purchasing. *British Medical Journal* 307:1436–1437.

Clinical Standards Advisory Group (1993a) *Access to and Availability of Specialist Services*. London: HMSO.

Clinical Standards Advisory Group (1993b) *Coronary Artery Bypass Grafting and Coronary Angioplasty.* London: HMSO.

Clinical Standards Advisory Group (1993c) *Cystic Fibrosis.* London: HMSO.

Clinical Standards Advisory Group (1993d) *Neonatal Intensive Care.* London: HMSO.

Clinical Standards Advisory Group (1993e) *Childhood Leukaemia.* London: HMSO.

Clinical Standards Advisory Group (1994a) *Standards of Clinical Care for People with Diabetes.* London: HMSO.

Clinical Standards Advisory Group (1994b) *The Epidemiology and Cost of Back Pain.* London: HMSO.

Clinical Standards Advisory Group (1994c) *Back Pain.* London: HMSO.

Clinical Standards Advisory Group (1994d) *Schizophrenia.* London: HMSO.

Clinical Standards Advisory Group (1995a) *Dental/General Anaesthesia.* London: HMSO.

Clinical Standards Advisory Group (1995b) *Women in Labour.* London: HMSO.

Clinical Standards Advisory Group (1995c) *Urgent and Emergency Admissions to Hospital.* London: HMSO.

Colgan E, Rose J (1997) The long and winding road. *Health Service Journal* 107(5580):28–29.

Committee of Public Accounts (1995) *General Practitioner Fundholding in England.* Minutes of Evidence. London: HMSO.

Consumers' Association (1995a) GPs: is your doctor a fundholder? *Which?* June:16–17.

Consumers' Association (1995b) GPs: what makes a good GP? *Which?* June: 18–19.

Cornell J (1996) Has general practice fundholding been good for patients? *Public Health* 110:5–6.

Corney R (1992) The effectiveness of counselling in general practice. *International Review of Psychiatry* 4:331–337.

Corney R (1994) Experience of first wave general practice fundholders in South East Thames Regional Health Authority. *British Journal of General Practice* 44:34–37.

Coulter A (1992) Fundholding general practices: early successes – but will they last? *British Medical Journal* 304:397–398.

Coulter A (1995a) Evaluating general practice fundholding in the UK. *European Journal of Public Health* 5:233–239.

Coulter A (1995b) Shifting the balance from secondary to primary care. *British Medical Journal* 311:1447–1448.

Coulter A (1995c) General practice fundholding: time for a cool appraisal. *British Journal of General Practice* 45:119–120.

Coulter A (1996) Why should health services be primary care-led? *Journal of Health Services Research and Policy* 1:122–124.

Coulter A, Bradlow J (1993) Effect of NHS reforms on general practitioners' referrals. *British Medical Journal* 306:433–436.

Crail M (1997) Crash test dummies. *Health Service Journal* 107 (5568):8–10.

Crump B, Cubbon J, Drummond M, Hawkes R, Marchment M (1991) Fundholding in general practice and financial risks. *British Medical Journal* 302:1582–1584.

Crump B, Panton R, Drummond MF, Marchment M, Hawkes RA (1995) Transferring the costs of expensive treatments from secondary to primary care. *British Medical Journal* 310:509–512.

Dawson D (1995) *Regulating Competition in the NHS*. Discussion Paper No. 131. York: Centre for Health Economics, University of York.

Department of Health (1991a) *The Patient's Charter*. London: HMSO.

Department of Health (1991b) *Local Voices*. London: HMSO.

Department of Health (1994) *A Guide to the Operation of the NHS Internal Market: Local Freedoms, National Responsibilities*. Leeds: NHS Executive.

Department of Health (1996a) *The Government's Expenditure Plans 1996/97 to 1998/99*. London: HMSO.

Department of Health (1996b) *Public Appointments Annual Report 1996*. London: HMSO.

Dixon J (1994) Can there be fair funding for fundholding practices? *British Medical Journal* 308:772–775.

Dixon J, Glennerster H (1995) What do we know about fundholding in general practice? *British Medical Journal* 311:727–730.

Dixon J, Dinwoodie M, Hudson D, Dodd S, Poltorak T, Garret C, Rice P, Doncaster I, Williams M (1994) Distribution of funds between fundholders and non-fundholding practices. *British Medical Journal* 309:30–34.

Dixon J, Mays N, Goodwin N (1998) *Accountability of Total Purchasing Pilot Projects*. National Evaluation of Total Purchasing Pilot Projects Working Paper. London: King's Fund.

Dixon M, Murray T, Jenner D, Pearson V (1996) *Is GP Commissioning Effective, and Does It Represent Value for Money?* Unpublished, Cullompton: Mid-Devon GP Commissioning Group.

Dowell J, Snaddon D, Dunbar J (1995) Changing to generic formulary: how one fundholding practice reduced prescribing costs. *British Medical Journal* 310:505–508.

Dowling B (1997) Effect of fundholding on waiting times: database study. *British Medical Journal* 315:290–292.

Drummond M, Teeling-Smith G, Wells N (1988) *Economic Evaluation on the Development of Medicines.* London: Office of Health Economics.

Ellwood S (1997) *The Response of Fundholding Doctors to the Market.* London: CIMA.

Enthoven A (1985) *Reflections on the Management of the NHS.* London: Nuffield Provincial Hospitals Trust.

Eve R, Hodgkin P (1991) In praise of non-fundholding practices. *British Medical Journal* 303:167–168.

Exworthy M (1993a) A review of recent structural changes to district health authorities as purchasing organisations. *Environment and Planning* 11:279–289.

Exworthy M (1993b) The development of purchasing: liaison with GPs. *Primary Care Management* 3:9–10.

Fear C, Cattell H (1994) Fundholding general practices and old age psychiatry. *Psychiatric Bulletin* 18:263–265.

Fisher A (1993) Fundholding. *British Medical Journal* 306:1003

Flynn R, Williams G (1997) Contracting for health. In: Flynn R, Williams G (Eds), *Contracting for Health: Quasi-markets and the National Health Service.* Oxford: Oxford University Press, 1–13.

Flynn R, Pickard S, Williams G (1995) Contracts and the quasi-market in community health services. *Journal of Social Policy*, 24:529–550.

Flynn R, Williams G, Pickard S (1996) *Markets and Networks: Contracting in Community Health Services*. Buckingham: Open University Press.

Foster C, Plowden J (1996) *The State under Stress*. Buckingham: Open University Press.

Fotaki M (1998) The impact of market-oriented reforms on patient choice and information: a case study of outer London and Stockholm. *Social Science and Medicine*. Forthcoming.

Francombe C (1991) *The NHS Reforms: the First Six Months*. Enfield: Middlesex Polytechnic, Health Research Centre.

Francombe C (1996) *Health Reforms and General Practices*. Enfield: Middlesex University Press.

Frater A, Dixon P (1994) *A Survey of Purchaser's Use of Health Outcome Assessment*. Leeds: UK Clearing House on Health Outcomes, Nuffield Institute for Health.

Freake D, Crowley P, Steiner M, Drinkwater C (1997) Local heroes. *Health Service Journal* 107(5561):28–29.

Freemantle N, Watt I, Mason J (1993) Developments in the purchasing process in the NHS: towards an explicit politics of rationing? *Public Administration* 71:535–548.

Fundholding (1991) Should you go private? 1:11–12.

Gaffney D, Pollock AM (1997) *Can the NHS Afford the Private Finance Initiative?* London: Health Policy and Economic Research Unit, British Medical Association.

Garrett C (1996) Trends in emergency admission in London. In: Boyle S (Ed.), *London Monitor: the Guide to Health Services in the Capital*, No. 3. London: King's Fund Publishing.

Gask L, Lee J, Donnan S, Roland M (1998) *Total Purchasing and Extended Fundholding of Mental Health Services*. National Evaluation of Total Purchasing Pilot Projects Working Paper. London: King's Fund.

Ghodse B (1995) Extracontractual referrals: safety valve or administrative paperchase? *British Medical Journal* 310:1573–1576.

Gill M (1993) Purchasing for quality: still in the starting blocks. *Quality in Health Care* 2:179–182.

Gillam S, Ball M, Prasad M, Dunne H, Cohen S, Vardis G (1995) An investigation of benefits and costs of an ophthalmic outreach clinic in general practice. *British Journal of General Practice* 45:649–652.

Gilmour I (1993) *Dancing with Dogma*. London: Simon and Schuster.

Glennerster H (1994) Future of fundholding. In: Harrison A (Ed), *Health Care UK 1993/94*. London: King's Fund.

Glennerster H, Le Grand J (1995) The development of quasi-markets in welfare provision in the United Kingdom. *International Journal of Health Services* 25:203–218.

Glennerster H, Matsaganis M, Owens P (1992) *A Foothold for Fundholding*. London: King's Fund Institute:74–107.

Glennerster H, Matsaganis M, Owens P (1994a) Implementing GP fundholding: wild card or winning hand? In: Robinson R, Le Grand J (Eds), *Evaluating the NHS Reforms*. London: King's Fund Institute.

Glennerster H, Matsaganis M, Owens P (1994b) *Implementing GP Fundholding: Wild Card or Winning Hand?* Buckingham: Open University Press.

Glennerster H, Cohen A, Bovell V (1996) *Alternatives to Fundholding*. WSP/123. London: STICERD, London School of Economics and Political Science.

Gosden T, Torgerson D, (1997) The effect of fundholding on prescribing and referral costs: a review of the evidence. *Health Policy* 40:103–114.

Government Statistical Service (1994) *NHS Hospital and Community Health Services: Non-medical Staff 1983–94*. London: Department of Health.

Government Statistical Service (1995) *NHS Hospital and Community Health Services: Non-Medical Staff*. London: Department of Health.

Graffy JP, Williams J (1994) Purchasing for all: an alternative to fundholding. *British Medical Journal* 308:391–394.

Grampian Asthma Study of Integrated Care (1994) Integrated care for asthma: a clinical, social and economic evaluation. *British Medical Journal* 308:599–604.

Green D, Neuberger J, Young Lord, Burstall M (1990) *The NHS Reforms: Whatever Happened to Consumer Choice?* London: IEA Health and Welfare Unit.

Greenhalgh P (1994) *Shared Care for Diabetes: a Systematic Review*. Occasional Paper 67. London: Royal College of General Practitioners.

Griffiths R (Chair) (1983) *NHS Management Inquiry*. London: Department of Health and Social Security.

Griffiths J (1996) *Defining the Essentials: the Functions, Roles and Costs of Health Authorities and GP Purchasers*. London and Milton Keynes: NHS Executive Anglia and Oxford, North Thames and South Thames.

Hacket G, Bundred P, Hutton J, O'Brian J, Stanley I (1993) Management of joint and soft tissue injuries in three general practices: value of on-site physiotherapy. *British Journal of General Practice* 43:61–64.

Ham C (1991a) *The Impact of the NHS Reforms on Health Authorities and Trusts*. Submission by the King's Fund to the House of Commons Select Committee on Health. London: King's Fund.

Ham C (1991b) Privatisation on parade. *British Medical Journal* 303:1099–1100.

Ham C (1992a) *Locality Purchasing.* Birmingham: Health Services Management Centre, The University of Birmingham.

Ham C (1992b) Local heroes. *Health Service Journal* 102(5329):20–21.

Ham C, Shapiro J (1995) *Integrating Purchasing: Lessons from Experience.* Discussion Paper 35. Birmingham: Health Services Management Centre, The University of Birmingham.

Ham C, Woolley M (1996) *How Does the NHS Measure Up? Assessing the Performance of Health Authorities.* Birmingham: National Association of Health Authorities and Trusts.

Hamblin R, Harrison A, Boyle S (1998) The wrong target. *Health Service Journal* 107(5598):26–31.

Harris A (1997) Specialist outreach clinics. *British Medical Journal* 308, 1053.

Harris C, Scrivener G (1996) Fundholders' prescribing costs: the first five years. *British Medical Journal* 313:1531–1534.

Harrison A (Ed.) (1993) *From Hierarchy to Contract.* Hermitage: Policy Journals.

Harrison A (1996) *Hospital Management in the UK.* Unpublished. London: King's Fund.

Harrison A (1997a) No way to manage. *Health Management* (June):28–29.

Harrison S (1997b) *The Worth Valley Health Consortium: Evaluation Report.* Leeds: Nuffield Institute for Health.

Harrison A, New B (1997) Health Policy Review. In: Harrison A (Ed.), *Health Care UK 1996/97.* London: King's Fund, 1–122.

Harrison A, Hamblin R, Boyle S, Tristem R, Pierce A (1995) *Analysing Changes in Emergency Admissions*. London: NHS Trust Federation, in association with the King's Fund.

Healey A, Reid J (1994) Do prospective fundholders inflate their prescribing costs? A study of Grampian fundholding and non-fundholding practices. *Health Bulletin* 52:282–284.

Health Service Journal (1992) In brief. 102(5305): 8.

Heaney D, Howie J, Maxwell M (1994) The referral component of fundholding: can both quantity and quality be assessed on routine data? *Health Bulletin* 52:285–296.

Hine C, Bachmann M (1997) What does locality commissioning in Avon offer? Retrospective descriptive evaluation. *British Medical Journal* 314:1246–1250.

Hoey A (1995) GP fundholding: mixing money and medicine. *Consumer Policy Review* 5:175–179.

House of Commons Health Committee (1994a) *First Special Report.* Memorandum from the Department of Health on Public Expenditure on Health and Personal Social Services, 14 July. Response by Virginia Bottomley MP to a question by Hugh Bayley MP. London: HMSO, 184–186.

House of Commons Health Committee (1994b) *Priority Setting in the NHS: Memoranda Received from Regional Health Authorities in Response to a Questionnaire from the Health Committee.* London: HMSO.

House of Commons Health Committee. (1995a) *Priority Setting in the NHS: Purchasing,* volume 1. London: HMSO.

House of Commons Health Committee. (1995b) *First Report. Long-term Care: NHS Responsibilities for Meeting Continuing Health Care Needs,* volume 1. London: HMSO.

Howie J, Heaney D, Maxwell M (1993) Evaluation of Scottish shadow fundholding project: first results. *Health Bulletin* 51:94–105.

Howie J, Heaney D, Maxwell M (1994) Evaluating care of patients reporting back pain in fundholding practices. *British Medical Journal* 309:705–710.

Howie J, Heaney D, Maxwell M (1995a) *General Practice Fund-holding: Shadow Project – an Evaluation*. Edinburgh: Department of General Practice, University of Edinburgh.

Howie J, Heaney D, Maxwell M (1995b) Care of patients with selected health problems in shadow fund-holding practices in Scotland in 1990 and 1992. *British Journal of General Practice* 45:119–120.

Hudson B (1996) Jointly or severally. *Health Service Journal* 106 (5499):26–27.

Hudson B, Willis J (1995) Analysis of joint commissioning developments in the northern regions. Leeds: Nuffield Institute for Health.

Hudson-Hart C, Drummond N, Deane M, Chopra R (1997) *Locality Commissioning: How Much Influence Do GPs Really Have?* (Abstract). Proceedings of the Society for Social Medicine 41st Annual Scientific Meeting. University of York: Journal of Epidemiology and Community Health, 5.

Hughes D, Griffiths L, McHale J (1997) Do quasi-markets evolve? Institutional analysis and the NHS. *Cambridge Journal of Economics* 21:259–76.

James A (1993) Access to specialty care in UK. *The Lancet* 342:109.

Jankowski RF, Bhatt R, Jenkins A (1997) GPs and health authority believe that locality commissioning will improve services. *British Medical Journal* 315:681–682.

Johnson S, Ramsay R, Thornicroft G, Brooks L, Lelliott P, Peck E, Smith H, Chisolm D, Audini B, Knapp M, Goldberg D (1997) *London's Mental Health*. London: King's Fund Publishing.

Jones D, Lester C, West R (1994) Monitoring changes in health services for older people. In: Le Grand J, Robinson R (Eds), *Evaluating the NHS Reforms*. London: King's Fund Institute, 130–154.

Judge K, Mulligan J, New B (1997) The NHS: new prescriptions needed? In: Jowell R, Curtice J, Park A, Brook L, Thompson K, Bryson C (Eds), *British Social Attitudes, 14th Report*. Aldershot: Dartmouth, 49–72.

Kammerling R, Kinnear A (1996) The extent of the two-tier service for fundholders. *British Medical Journal* 312:1399–1401.

Keeley D (1993) The fundholding debate: should practices reconsider the decision not to fundhold? *British Medical Journal* 306:607–698.

Kerrison S, Corney R (1998) Private provision of 'outreach' clinics to fundholding general practices in England. *Journal of Health Services Research and Policy* 3:20–22.

Kind P, Leese B, Hardman G (1992) *Evaluating the Fundholding Initiative: the Views of General Practitioners*. York: Centre for Health Economics, University of York.

Kind P, Leese B, Hardman G (1993a) *Evaluating the Fund holding Initiative: Variations in Prescribing Patterns*. York: Centre for Health Economics, University of York.

Kind P, Leese B, Hardman G (1993b) *Evaluating the Fund holding Initiative: the Views of Patients*. York: Centre for Health Economics, University of York.

King M, Brosker G, Lloyd M, Horder J (1994) Controlled trials in the evaluation of counselling in general practice. *British Journal of General Practice* 44:229–232.

Kingman S (1992) Hospitals slow down as money runs out. *British Medical Journal* 306:227–229.

Kirkup B, Donaldson LJ (1994) Is health care a commodity?: how will purchasing improve the National Health Service? *Journal of Public Health Medicine* 16:256–262.

Klein, R (1995a) *The New Politics of the National Health Service*, third edition. London: Longman.

Klein R (1995b) Self-inventing institutions: institutionalised design and the UK welfare state. In: Goodin RE, (Ed), *The Theory of Institutionalised Design*. Cambridge: Cambridge University Press, 240–255.

Klein R, Redmayne S (1992) *Patterns of Priorities: a Study of the Purchasing and Rationing Policies of Health Authorities*. Birmingham: Health Services Management Centre, University of Birmingham, National Association of Health Authorities and Trusts.

Labour Party (1992) *No Previous Experience Required: a Survey of Third Wave NHS Trusts*. London: Labour Party.

Labour Party (1994) *350% More Spent on Cars by Trusts*. London: Labour Party.

Layzell A (1994) Local and vocal. *Health Service Journal* 104(5386):28–30.

Leese B, Bosanquet N (1996) Changes in general practice organisation: survey of general practitioners' views on the 1990 contract and fundholding. *British Medical Journal* 46:95–99.

Le Grand J (1991) *Equity and Choice*. London: HarperCollins.

Le Grand J (1997) Knights, knaves or pawns? Human behaviour and social policy. *Journal of Social Policy* 26:146–169.

Le Grand J, Bartlett W (1993) *Quasi-markets and Social Policy*. London: Macmillan.

Le Grand J, Vizard P (1998) The National Health Service: crisis, change or continuity? In: Glennerster H, Hills J (Eds), *The State of Welfare*, second edition. Oxford: Oxford University Press, 75–121.

Lenaghan J, New B, Mitchell E (1996) Setting priorities: is there a role for citizens' juries? *British Medical Journal* 312:1591–1593.

Light DW (1994) *Strategic Challenges in Joint Commissioning*. London: North West Thames Regional Health Authority.

Lindblom C (1979) Still muddling, not yet through. *Public Administration Review* 39(5):7–25.

London Health Economics Consortium (1996) *Innovation and Contracting*. London: London Health Economics Consortium, London School of Hygiene and Tropical Medicine.

Ludlam C, Hay C, Dolan G (1997) Treatment for haemophilia by postcode (letter). *British Medical Journal* 344:749.

Luxton D (1993) Fundholding practices get preference. *British Medical Journal* 306:206–207.

Macrae Todd E (1993) Should consultants do sessions in GPFH practices? A GP's view. *British Journal of Hospital Medicine* 50:636–637.

Mahon A, Wilkin D, Whitehouse C (1994) Choice of hospital for elective surgery referrals: GPs' and patients' views. In: Robinson R, Le Grand J (Eds), *Evaluating the NHS Reforms*. London: King's Fund Institute, 108–129.

Mahon A. Leese B, Stoddart H, Baxter K (1998) *How do Total Purchasing Pilot Projects Inform Themselves for Purchasing?* National Evaluation of Total Purchasing Pilot Projects Working Paper. London: King's Fund.

Majeed F, Chaturvedi N, Reading R, Ben-Shlomo Y (1994) Monitoring and promoting equity in primary and secondary care. *British Medical Journal* 308:1426–1429.

Marks D (1995) *NHS Reforms: the First Three Years: a Survey of Directors of Public Health*. London: Middlesex University, Health Research Centre.

Marum M (1997) Fundholding has curbed increases in prescribing costs (letter). *British Medical Journal* 315:748–749.

Marwick J (1994) *Report on GP Fundholding Developments in the UK.* Wellington: New Zealand Ministry of Health, Manatu Hauora.

Maxwell M, Heaney D, Howie J (1993) General practice fundholding: observations on prescribing patterns and costs using the defined daily dose method. *British Medical Journal* 307:1190–1194.

May A (1989) A guru vexed by his government disciples. *Health Service Journal* 99:1150.

Maynard A (1986) Performance incentives in general practice. In: Teeling-Smith G (Ed), *Health Education and General Practice.* London: Office of Health Economics.

Maynard A, Bloor K (1995) Primary care and health care reform: the need to reflect before reforming. *Health Policy* 31:171–181.

Maynard A, Bloor K (1996) Introducing a market to the United Kingdom's National Health Service. *New England Journal of Medicine* 334:604–608.

Mays N, Dixon J (1996) *Purchaser Plurality in UK Health Care: Is a Consensus Emerging and Is It the Right One?* London: King's Fund Publishing.

Mays N, Goodwin N, Bevan G, Wyke S (1997) What is total purchasing? *British Medical Journal* 315:652–655.

Mays N, Goodwin N, Killoran A, Malbon G, on behalf of the Total Purchasing National Evaluation Team (1998a) *Total Purchasing: a Step towards Primary Care Groups.* London: King's Fund.

Mays N, Goodwin N, Malbon G, Leese B, Mahon A, Wyke S (1998b) *What Were the Achievements of Total Purchasing Pilots in Their First Year and How Can They Be Explained?* Total Purchasing National Evaluation Team Working Paper. London: King's Fund.

McAvoy B (1993) Heartsink hotel revisited. *British Medical Journal* 306:694–695.

McCullough C (1993) Fundholding practices get preference (letter). *British Medical Journal* 306:1411

McKee M, Clarke A (1995) Guidelines, enthusiasms, uncertainty and the limits to purchasing. *British Medical Journal* 310:101–104.

Milhil C (1993) Ministers back patient inequalities. *The Guardian* October 10: 5.

Millar B (1997) Nine-to-five. *Health Service Journal* 107(5535):12–13.

Moonie L, Galbraith S (1989) *'Working for Patients': a Critique*. Scotland: Labour Party.

Moore L, Dalziel M (1993) Making the internal market work: a case for managed change. *British Medical Journal* 307:1720–1722.

Muijen M, Ford R (1996) The market and mental health: intentional and unintentional incentives. *Journal of Interprofessional Care* 10:13–22.

Mulligan J, Judge K (1997) Public opinion and the NHS. In: Harrison A (Ed.), *Health Care UK, 1996/97*. London: King's Fund Publishing, 123–137.

Murray D (1993) *Partners in NHS Commissioning? A Review and Discussion of Alternative Models of Integrated Locally Sensitive Commissioning*. Unpublished MSc Dissertation. London: London School of Hygiene and Tropical Medicine.

National Audit Office (1994) *General Practitioner Fundholding in England*. London: HMSO.

Newbronner L (1996) *Evaluation of Primary Care 2000: the Process of Implementation and the Early Operation of the Project*. York: York Health Economics Consortium, University of York.

Newton J, Fraser M, Robinson J, Wainwright D (1993) Fundholding in Northern Region: the first year. *British Medical Journal* 306:375–378.

NHS Consultants' Association Health Policy Network (1995) *In Practice: the NHS Market.* Banbury: NHS Consultants' Association.

NHS Executive (1994a) *Developing NHS Purchasing and GP Fundholding: towards a Primary Care-led NHS.* EL (94)79. Leeds: NHSE.

NHS Executive (1994b) *The Accountability Framework for GP Fundholding.* Leeds: NHS Executive.

NHS Executive (1994c) *Annual Report, 1993/94.* Leeds: NHS Executive.

NHS Executive (1995) *Annual Report, 1994/95.* Leeds: NHS Executive.

NHS Executive (1996) *Health Authority Costs.* Leeds: NHS Executive.

NHS Executive (1997) *GP Commissioning Groups.* Leeds: NHS Executive.

NHS Management Executive (1991) *NHS reforms: the first six months.* London: NHS Management Executive.

NHS Management Executive (1992) *Local Voices: the Views of Local People in Purchasing for Health.* London: NHS Management Executive.

Nottingham Non-Fundholders (1996) *The Future of Commissioning in Nottingham.* Unpublished proceedings from Annual General Meeting, 22 May, Nottingham: Nottingham Non-Fundholders.

Office of Health Economics (1995) *Compendium of Health Statistics.* London: Office of Health Economics.

Office for Public Management (1994) *Kensington, Chelsea and Westminster Commissioning Agency: the North East Westminster Locality Purchasing Project.* London: Office for Public Management.

Osborne D, Gaebler T (1992) *Reinventing Government.* Massachusetts: Addison Wesley.

Packwood T, Keen J, Buxton M (1991) *Hospitals in Transition: the Resource Management Experiment.* Buckingham: Open University Press.

Paton C (1992) *Competition and Planning in the NHS: the Danger of Unplanned Markets.* London: Chapman & Hall.

Paton C (1995) Present dangers and future threats: some perverse incentives in the NHS reforms. *British Medical Journal* 310:1245–1248.

Pauly M (1986) Taxation, health insurance and market failure in the medical economy. *Journal of Economic Literature* 24:629–675.

Peeke A (1993) *Waiting Times for GP Fundholder Procedures.* Oxford: Oxford Regional Health Authority.

Penhale D, Lis Y, Richardson J, McGuire A (1993) *A Comparison of First-wave Fundholding and Non-fundholding Practices.* Unpublished paper presented to the Health Economics Study Group Meeting, 23 July.

Pennington S (1995) GPs enter first total commissioning scheme. *GP* 21 April:28.

Petchey R (1993) The NHS internal market 1991–2: towards a balance sheet. *British Medical Journal* 306:699–701.

Petchey R (1995) General practitioner fundholding: weighing the evidence. *The Lancet* 346:1139–1142.

Petchey R (1997) Just what the doctor ordered? *Journal of Social Policy* 16:489–507.

Pettigrew A, Ferlie E, McKee L (1992) *Managing Strategic Change.* London: Sage.

Pickard S, Williams G, Flynn R (1995) Local voices in an internal market: the case of community health services. *Social Policy and Administration* 29:135–149.

Pickin C, Popay J (1994) *Locality Approaches in Purchasing: a Review of Current Practice in the NHS.* Salford: Public Health Research and Resource Centre, University of Salford.

Posnett J, Goodwin N, Griffiths J, Killoran A, Malbon G, Mays N, Place M, Street A (1998) *The Transactions Costs of Total Purchasing.* National Evaluation of Total Purchasing Pilot Project Working Paper. London: King's Fund.

Primary Care Support Force (1996) *What Works Well? What needs to Happen?* London: Primary Care Support Force.

Propper C (1995a) Agency and incentives in the NHS internal market. *Social Science and Medicine* 40:1683–1690.

Propper C (1995b) Regulatory reform of the NHS internal market. *Health Economics* 4:71–83.

Propper C, Bartlett W (1997) The impact of competition on the behaviour of National Health Service Trusts. In: Flynn R, Williams G (Eds), *Contracting for Health: Quasi-markets and the National Health Service.* Oxford: Oxford University Press, 115–134.

Purchasing in Practice (1995) The effects of fundholding on prescribing. 6:18–19.

Radical Statistics Health Group (1992a) NHS Reforms: the first six months – proof of progress or a statistical smokescreen? *British Medical Journal* 304:705–709.

Radical Statistics Health Group (1992b) *A Growing Health Service?* London: Radical Statistics.

Radical Statistics Health Group (1995) NHS 'indicators of success': what do they tell us? *British Medical Journal* 310:1045–1050.

Rafferty T, Wilson-Davis K, McGavoek H (1997) How has fundholding in Northern Ireland affected prescribing patterns? A longitudinal study. *British Medical Journal* 315:166–170.

Raftery J, Mulligan J, Forrest S, Robinson R (1994) *Third Review of Contracting*. Leeds: NHS Executive.

Raftery J, McLeod H (1998) *Hospital Activity Changes and Total Purchasing*. National Evaluation of Total Purchasing Pilot Projects Working Paper. London: King's Fund.

Reading R, Jarvis S, Openshaw S (1993) Measurement of social inequalities in health and use of health services among children in Northumberland. *Archives of Disease in Childhood* 68:626–631.

Redmayne S, Klein R, Day P (1993) *Sharing out Resources: Purchasing and Priority Setting in the NHS*. Birmingham: Health Services Management Centre, University of Birmingham, National Association of Health Authorities and Trusts.

Redmayne S (1995) *Reshaping the NHS: Strategies, Priorities and Resource Allocation*. Birmingham: Health Services Management Centre, University of Birmingham, National Association of Health Authorities and Trusts.

Redmayne S (1996) *Small steps, big goals: purchasing policies in the NHS*. Bath: Centre for the Analysis of Social Policy, University of Bath.

Roberts JA (1993) Managing markets. *Journal of Public Health Medicine* 15:305–310.

Robinson E (1996) Other factors probably explain difference in prescribing. *British Medical Journal* 312:849.

Robinson R, Le Grand J (Eds) (1994) *Evaluating the NHS Reforms*. London: King's Fund Institute.

Robinson R, Robison J, Raftery J (1998) *Contracting by Total Purchasing Pilot Projects, 1996/97*. National Evaluation of Total Purchasing Pilot Projects Working Paper. London: King's Fund.

Roland M (1991) Fundholding and cash limits in primary care: blight or blessing? *British Medical Journal* 303:171–172.

Salfield N (1997) Ending in tiers. *Health Service Journal* 107(5568): 24–25.

Samuel O (1992) Fundholding practices get preference (letter). *British Medical Journal* 305:1497.

Scheffler R (1989) Adverse selection: the Achilles heel of the NHS reforms. *The Lancet* i:950–952.

Scheuer M, Robinson R (1991) A wild card in the pack. *Health Service Journal* 101(5264):18–20.

Scott A, Shiell A, King M (1996) Is general practitioner decision making associated with patient socio-economic status? *Social Science and Medicine* 42:35–46.

Secretaries of State for Health, Northern Ireland, Wales and Scotland (1989) *Working for Patients*. CM55. London: HMSO.

Secretary of State for Health (1996a) *Choice and Opportunity*. CM3390. London: HMSO.

Secretary of State for Health (1996b) *Delivering the Future*. CM 3512. London: HMSO.

Secretary of State for Health (1997) *The New NHS – Modern, Dependable*. CM 3807. London: HMSO.

Seng C, Lessof L, McKee M (1993) Who's on the fiddle? *Health Service Journal* 103(5334):16–17.

Shaoul J (1996) *NHS Trusts – a Capital Way of Operating*. Mimeo, Manchester: University of Manchester, Department of Accounting and Finance.

Shapiro J (1994) *Shared Purchasing and Collaborative Commissioning within the NHS*. Birmingham: Health Service Management Centre, University of Birmingham, National Association of Health Authorities and Trusts.

Shapiro J, Smith J, Walsh N (1996) *Approaches to Commissioning: the Dynamics of Diversity*. Birmingham: Health Service Management Centre, University of Birmingham, National Association of Health Authorities and Trusts.

Sheldon TA, Borowitz M (1993) Changing the measure of quality in the NHS: from purchasing activity to purchasing protocols. *Quality in Health Care* 2:149–150.

Shiell A (1992) Competing hospitals: assessing the impact of self-governing trust status in the UK. *Health Policy* 19:141–158.

Smee C (1995) Self-governing trusts and GP fundholders: the British experience. In: Saltman R, Von Otter C (Eds), *Implementing Planned Markets in Healthcare*. Buckingham: Open University Press, 177–208.

Smith J, Bamford M, Ham C, Scrivens E, Shapiro J (1997a) *Beyond Fundholding: a Mosaic of Primary Care Led Commissioning and Provision in the West Midlands*. Birmingham: Health Services Management Centre, University of Birmingham.

Smith J, Barnes M, Ham C, Martin G (1997b) *Mapping Approaches to Commissioning: Extending the Mosaic*. Birmingham: Health Services Management Centre, University of Birmingham.

Smith J, Shapiro J (1996) *Holding on While Letting Go*. Birmingham: Health Services Management Centre, University of Birmingham.

Smith J, Shapiro J (1997) Local call. *Health Service Journal* 107(5535):26–27.

Smith P (1993) Outcome-related performance indicators and organizational control in the public sector. *British Journal of Management* 4:135–151.

Söderlund N, Csba I, Gray A, Milne R, Raftery J. (1997) Impact of the NHS reforms on English hospital productivity: an analysis of the first three years. *British Medical Journal* 315:1126–29.

South Bucks Community Health Council (1994) *GP Referral Survey.* High Wycombe: South Bucks Community Health Council.

Spurgeon P, Smith P, Straker M, Deakin N, Thomas N, Walsh K (1997) The experience of contracting in health care. In: Flynn R, Williams G (Eds), *Contracting for Health: Quasi-markets and the National Health Service.* Oxford: Oxford University Press, 135–152.

Stevens A, Colin-Jones D, Gabbay J (1995) 'Quick and clean': authoritative health technology assessment for local health care contracting. *Health Trends* 27:37–42.

Stewart-Brown S, Surender R, Bradlow J, Coulter A (1995) The effects of fundholding in general practice on prescribing habits three years after the introduction of the scheme. *British Medical Journal* 311:1543–1547.

Strawderman T, Mays N, Goodwin N (1996) *Review of NHS Executive Regional Total Purchasing Lead Officers.* Unpublished. Total Purchasing National Evaluation Team Working Paper. London: King's Fund.

Surender R, Bradlow J, Coulter A, Doll H, Stewart-Brown S (1995) Prospective study of trends in referral patterns in fundholding and non-fundholding practices in the Oxford region, 1990–94. *British Medical Journal* 311:1205–1208.

Taylor P (1991) The implications of general practice fundholding. *Health Direct* 8, 6–7.

Thatcher M (1990) *The Downing Street Years.* London: HarperCollins.

The Independent (1996) Non-smoking GP dumps 60-a-day arthritis patient. 26 February.

Timmins N (1995a) *The Five Giants.* London: HarperCollins.

Timmins N (1995b) GPs' cash gains a wok shop. *The Independent* February 28: 6.

Total Purchasing National Evaluation Team (1997) *Total Purchasing: a Profile of National Pilot Projects.* London: King's Fund.

Toth B, Harvey I, Peters T (1997) Did the introduction of general practice fundholding change patterns of emergency admission to hospital? *Journal of Health Services Research and Policy* 2:71–74.

Traynor M (1995) *A Study of Three NHS Trusts: the Managers' Accounts.* London: Royal College of Nursing.

Trimble D, Black I (1996) Prescribing by general practice fundholders. *British Medical Journal* 312:848–849.

University of Surrey (1993) *Population Health Outcome Indicators for the NHS 1993: England: a Consultation Document.* London: Department of Health.

Wainwright D (1996) *Primary Care Led Commissioning in East Kent.* Canterbury: Centre for Health Services Studies, University of Kent.

Wall A (1994) Trusts: the reasons to be cautious. *Health Services Management Research* 7:187–194.

Wall A (1996) Mine, yours, or theirs?: accountability in the new NHS. *Policy and Politics* 24:73–84.

Walsh D (1995) The internal market in health: sham or saviour? *British Journal of Health Care Management* 1:352–355.

Walsh N, Shapiro J, Davidge M, Raftery J (1997) *Berkshire Integrated Purchasing Project: First Year Report: 'No Quick Fix'*. Birmingham: Health Services Management Centre, University of Birmingham.

Ware J (1986) Comparisons of health outcomes at a health maintenance organisation with use of fee-for-service care. *Lancet* i:1017–1022.

Warnes A (1997) *The Health and Care of Older People in London*. London: King's Fund.

Watson P (1994) Public health medicine and DHA members: a crucial interface in purchasing. In: Harrison S, Freemantle N (Eds), *Working for Patients: Early Research Findings*. Leeds: Nuffield Institute for Health, 61–90.

West PA (1997) *Understanding the National Health Service Reforms*. Buckingham: Open University Press.

Whitehead M (1994) Is it fair? Evaluating the equity implications of the NHS reforms. In: Robinson R, Le Grand J (Eds), *Evaluating the NHS Reforms*. London: King's Fund Institute, 208–242.

Whitty P, Jones I (1992) Public health heresy: a challenge to the purchasing orthodoxy. *British Medical Journal* 304:1039–1041.

Whynes D (1993) The internal market: economic aspects of its medium-term development. *International Journal of Health Planning and Management* 8:107–122.

Whynes D, Baines D, Tolley K (1995) GP fundholding and the costs of prescribing. *Journal of Public Health Medicine* 17:323–329.

Williams G, Flynn R (1997) Health-care contracting and social science: issues in theory and practice. In: Flynn R, Williams G (Eds), *Contracting for Health: Quasi-markets and the National Health Service*. Oxford: Oxford University Press, 153–159.

Willis A (1992) Who needs fundholding? *Health Service Journal* 102 (5300):24–26.

Willis A (1996) Commissioning – the best for all. In: Littlejohn P, Victor C (Eds), *Making Sense of a Primary Care-led Health Service*, Oxford: Radcliffe Medical Press, 67–75.

Wilson R, Buchan I, Walley T (1995) Alterations in prescribing by general practitioner fundholders: an observational study. *British Medical Journal* 311:1347–1350.

Wilson R, Walley T (1995) Prescribing costs in general practice fundholding. *Lancet* 346:1710–1711.

Wisely I (1993) General practice fundholding: experiences in Grampian. *British Medical Journal* 306:695–697.

Wright J (1994) Fundholding in general practice: early experiences in one region. In: Harrison S, Freemantle N (Eds), *Working for Patients: Early Research Findings*, Leeds: Nuffield Institute for Health, 91–122.

Young H (1993) *One of Us*. London: Pan Books Ltd.

Yule B, Healey A, Grimshaw J (1994) Fundholding: the next five years. *Journal of Public Health Medicine* 16:36–40.